We appreciate your order!

It is our goal to exceed your expectations!
Please take a few moments to let us know
what you think about our products and services.

Return this survey for a chance to win a $100 gift certificate for use toward any Region 4 product!*

*One winner drawn monthly. Winners announced at www.region4store.com and notified by email.

Name _____ Title _____

District _____ School _____

Address _____

City _____ State _____ Zip _____

Daytime Phone _____ Email _____

Grade(s) you teach _____

Product Title _____

PRODUCTS: 4=Excellent 3=Good 2=Fair 1=Poor					COMMENTS
1. Quality of product	4	3	2	1	
2. Satisfaction with product(s)	4	3	2	1	
3. Would you recommend this product to others?	☐ Yes ☐ No				

Additional space for comments is available on the back of this survey.

We would like to share your positive comments about us with other customers
Please indicate if we have your permission to use your comments on future promotional materials.

☐ Yes ☐ No

region4
Educated Solutions
Region 4 Education Service Center

Questions or Comments?
Call Customer Service at 713-744
or Fax 713-744-4444

Fold here.

Please be sure to seal the top of this survey using tape, not staples.

Help Us Help You!

Do you have any additional comments?

_____

_____

Do you have any additional product needs?

_____

_____

☐ Check if you would like to have a sales representative contact you.

Making Math Accessible
for English Language Learners:

Practical Tips and Suggestions

(Grades 9-12)

A Region 4 ESC Resource
Region 4 Education Service Center
Houston, TX

ABOUT THE REGION 4 EDUCATION SERVICE CENTER

The Region 4 Education Service Center (ESC) supports student achievement by providing educational products and services that focus on Excellence, Service, and Children. We create and conduct professional development institutes, produce research-based instructional materials, and provide technical assistance to strengthen educational systems to promote the academic success of all students.

First printing, April 2006
ISBN 1-933049-44-8

Additional Products and Services

Please visit our website www.esc4.net to view other products and services provided by Region 4 ESC.

Bill McKinney, Ph.D. Executive Director • Region 4 ESC is an equal opportunity employer.

Additional Region 4 ESC Resources

Mathematics

- TAKS Mathematics Preparation Grades K through Grade 11 Exit
- Mathematical Models with Applications Course Materials: Algebra II Alignment
- Making Connections with Measurement Grades K through Grade 11 Exit
- Accelerated Curriculum for Mathematics Grade 5 and Grade 11 Exit
- Integrating Grade 11 Geometry TAKS Objectives into Algebra II
- Making Math Accessible for English Language Learners Grades K-2, Grades 3-5, Grades 6-8
- Making Math Accessible to Students with Special Needs: Implementing TEKS, TAKS, and SDAAII
- Learning to Read/Reading to Learn—Mathematics Elementary School, Middle School, High School
- Scope and Sequence with Curriculum-Based Assessments: Mathematics for Grades K through Algebra II
- Mathematics Assessment Database CD Volume I Grades 1 through Algebra II
- Mathematics Assessment Database CD Volume II Grades K through Algebra II
- TAKS Simulation Math Assessments Grades K through Grade 11 Exit

Science

- TAKS Science Preparation Grades 2-5 Elementary, Grade 10, and Grade 11 Exit
- Gateways to Science Grades 6 through 8
- Warm Up to Science TEKS-based Engagement Activities Series Grade 5, Grade 8, Integrated Physics and Chemistry, Biology
- Accelerated Curriculum for Science Grade 11
- Scope and Sequence with Curriculum-Based Assessments: Science Grades K-8, Integrated Physics and Chemistry, Biology
- Reading to Learn in Science Grades 3-5, Grades 6-8, Grades 9-12
- Grade 1 Science and Math Children's Book entitled Which Pet Measures Up?
- Science Assessment Database Grades 1 through 5, Integrated Physics and Chemistry, Biology
- TAKS Simulation Science Assessments Grades 5, Grade 8, Grade 10, Grade 11 Exit

Social Studies

- TAKS Social Studies Preparation Grade 8, Grade 10, and Grade 11 Exit
- Reading to Learn in Social Studies Grades 6-8, Grades 9-12
- Resources for Librarians and Teachers
- Warm Up to Social Studies TEKS-based Engagement Activities Series Grade 11 Exit
- Scope and Sequence with Curriculum-Based Assessments for Grades 5 – 8, American History Studies, World History Studies, and World Geography Studies
- Social Studies Assessment Database Grades 5 through 8, Grade 10, Grade 11
- TAKS Simulation Social Studies Assessments Grades 5, Grade 8, Grade 10, Grade 11 Exit

Reading

- TAKS Reading Preparation Grade 3 through Grade 11 Exit
- Accelerated Curriculum for Reading Grade 3, Grade 5, and Middle School
- Scope and Sequence with Curriculum-Based Assessments Grades K through English III
- TAKS Simulation Assessments for Reading and English Language Arts Grades 3 through Grade 11 Exit

Go to www.esc4.net for complete descriptions, samples, and order forms.

Acknowledgements
Making Math Accessible for English Language Learners: *Practical Tips and Suggestions* Grades 9-12

Project Directors:
- Donna Landrith, Education Specialist, Mathematics
  Region 4 Education Service Center
- David Eschberger, Director, Mathematics Services
  Region 4 Education Service Center
- Jo Ann Wheeler, Managing Director, Project Development
  Region 4 Education Service Center

Authors:
Lead Author
- Donna Landrith, Education Specialist, Mathematics
  Region 4 Education Service Center
Contributing Authors
- Sharon Benson, Senior Education Specialist, Mathematics Services
  Region 4 Education Service Center
- David Eschberger, Director, Mathematics Services
  Region 4 Education Service Center
- Gary Cosenza, Independent Mathematics Consultant

Technical Support:
- Genelle Moore, Mathematics Services
  Region 4 Education Service Center
- Amanda Chilton, Mathematics Services
  Region 4 Education Service Center

Editors:
- Deborah S. Fitzgerald, Mathematics Department Chair
  Cypress-Fairbanks I.S.D.
- Martha P. Parham, High School Language Arts
  Cypress-Fairbanks I.S.D.

Table of Contents

Making Math Accessible for English Language Learners: *Practical Tips and Suggestions* Grades 9-12

region 4
Educated Solutions

Introduction

Population

Nearly one in five Americans speaks a language other than English at home, and almost 45 percent of U.S. teachers have at least one **Limited English Proficient (LEP)** student in class (National Symposium on Learning Disabilities in English Language Learners, 2003). In 2005, over 330,000 LEP students in Texas were assessed using the **Texas English Language Proficiency Assessment System (TELPAS)**. Of the 330,000 LEP students assessed with TELPAS in 2005, about 190,000 were also tested in 2004. Over 100,000 of them advanced less than one proficiency level from 2004 to 2005. More than 133,000 of those tested had been enrolled in U. S. schools more than 5 years, and approximately 60,000 of those enrolled for over 3 years were still at the Beginning or Intermediate levels. Approximately 94% of those tested were Hispanic (Texas Education Agency, 2005b).

TELPAS Results

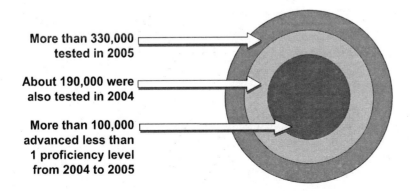

More than 330,000 tested in 2005

About 190,000 were also tested in 2004

More than 100,000 advanced less than 1 proficiency level from 2004 to 2005

The numbers referenced above include only students who returned Home Language Surveys indicating a language other than English was the primary language spoken at home. There are also some parents who choose not to receive services for their children for a variety of reasons, including their belief that the child will learn English faster if he is exposed only to English. These factors mean there are more students struggling to learn English than are assessed under TELPAS. The number of unofficial English language learners is further increased by the large number of students whose command of English is below the level necessary to succeed academically and by students whose primary language is English but whose use of the language is non-standard. We will use the term **English language learners (ELLs)** to encompass not only LEP students but also the larger group of students striving for proficiency in English.

As early as 1974, the U. S. Supreme Court ruled (Lau v Nichols) that all students, including English language learners, must be given equal access to the core curriculum. Even so, English language learners frequently were enrolled in low-level math classes in which the emphasis was on computation, ignoring the importance of language development in mathematics. Those enrolled in regular math classes were generally left to struggle with little support. Those who did not understand squeaked by or failed the course and repeated it. There was no "high-stakes" test required for graduation.

region *4*
Educated Solutions

Introduction

Assessment

Required state-wide testing was initiated in 1979 with the Texas Assessment of Basic Skills (TABS), which emphasized basic computation. The testing evolved from TABS to the Texas Educational Assessment of Minimal Skills (TEAMS), and for the first time, beginning with the graduating class of 1987, students who did not pass were denied diplomas. The difficulty level increased with the Texas Assessment of Academic Skills (TAAS), which was first administered in the fall of 1990 and placed more emphasis on problem-solving skills. Students could be coached to pass TAAS using drill and practice worksheets directed at a limited set of skills that topped out at the eighth-grade level.

The State raised the bar to its highest level yet with the Texas Assessment of Knowledge and Skills (TAKS), first required as a graduation standard with the graduating class of 2005. The Exit-Level Grade 11 Math TAKS requires students to demonstrate proficiency in not only the eighth-grade Texas Essential Knowledge and Skills (TEKS) involving proportion, percent, probability and statistics, and underlying processes and skills, but they must demonstrate proficiency in the Algebra I TEKS and Geometry TEKS. No Child Left Behind (NCLB) has increased the sense of urgency on the part of school administrators to ensure that all students, including ELLs, are successful. LEP students in Grades 3-8 and 10 may be given TAKS with the assistance of Linguistically Accommodated Testing (LAT), but LAT is not available in Grades 9 and 11.

Since the implementation of TAKS, LEP students have consistently scored considerably below non-LEP, non-monitored students. You will notice in the table that at grades 9, 10 and 11, LEP students not only scored below their classmates, but the gap is not closing.

Grade	Year	Percent Met Standard Non-LEP	Percent Met Standard LEP	LEP vs. Non-LEP Percent
9	2005	59	18	-41
	2004	61	21	-40
	2003	85	31	-54
10	2005	61	18	-43
	2004	65	27	-38
	2003	75	43	-32
11	2005	82	49	-33
	2004	86	59	-27
	2003	70	33	-37

It is important to understand that Texas students in Grade 3 through 11 (Exit), including LEP students, are assessed in mathematics using the Mathematics TAKS unless they qualify for Special Education and are exempt or assessed using an alternative test. Unless a student is classified as Limited English Proficient, he/she is assessed in Reading or English Language Arts, depending on the grade level, using TAKS as the assessment tool. Only English language learners classified as LEP are assessed using TELPAS.

The increasing pressure on district and campus administrators to achieve adequate yearly progress translates to increasing pressure on teachers to ensure all students demonstrate proficiency on TAKS. However, the greater rigor of the mathematics curricula and tests comes at a time when the number of ELLs continues to increase. So how is it possible for ELLs to succeed in mathematics and demonstrate proficiency on the TAKS when the student does not comprehend English?

Programs

Several secondary programs in Texas schools are designed to support Limited English Proficient students. **Bilingual Education** encompasses several programs which all provide at least some instruction in the student's primary language, including:

- Newcomer programs,
- Dual language,
- Two-way immersion,
- Transitional bilingual, and
- Heritage language preservation.

Bilingual teachers are trained in second language acquisition theory and are bilingual in English and the primary language of second language learners. In Texas, if a teacher has a bilingual endorsement, it is not necessary to have English as a Second Language (ESL) endorsement. Bilingual teachers focus on content area instruction, such as mathematics, in order to build conceptual academic knowledge in second language learners.

Bilingual education is not mandated beyond sixth grade, and though some districts opt to include bilingual education at the secondary level, most rely on English as a Second Language (ESL), sheltered instruction, structured English immersion, and, unfortunately, submersion.

In **English as a Second Language (ESL)** pull-out programs, students spend part of the day in a mainstream classroom and are "pulled out" for a portion of the day to receive instruction in English as a second language. ESL teachers are educators trained in second language acquisition theory and have professional endorsement through the Texas Education Agency. They can be utilized at all grade levels and generally focus on helping Limited English Proficient (LEP) students to develop academic language proficiency (TEA, 2004a).

Sheltered Instruction is an approach used for teaching language and content to English language learners. All academic subjects are taught in English using specific strategies that make content comprehensible to students and promote language development. Although the teachers may be ESL certified, it is more likely they have received required professional development in sheltered instruction strategies (TEA, 2004a).

In **Structured English Immersion** programs, classroom conversations are conducted in English. Immersion is structured, planned, and intentionally provides a context for new language acquisition using visuals and manipulatives (TEA, 2004).

Submersion is neither English as a Second Language nor a program. This model does not comply with Texas law and is merely a do-nothing approach that places English language learners in classes that are conducted solely in English without support for the student or the teacher (TEA, 2004a).

Making Math Accessible for English Language Learners is written to provide practical classroom tips and suggestions to strengthen the quality of classroom instruction for teachers in the scenarios described above. The tips and suggestions are based on research in practices and strategies that address the affective, linguistic, and cognitive needs of English language learners. Although the book is centered on teaching English language learners, many of the tips and suggestions are beneficial to all students. We will follow five case studies of composite student profiles throughout the book with opportunities for **Reflection** to increase personal awareness of both the teacher's role and students' needs in the mathematics classroom, **Tasks** to provide interaction with the content of the book, and **Hot Tips** for implementing the ideas in real-world situations.

Introduction

Part I of *Making Math Accessible for English Language Learners* lays the foundation for working with English language learners in mathematics classrooms. In Chapter 1, we will focus on the **Challenges** facing teachers in their classrooms as they work to ensure the success of English language learners. We will introduce the students in the case studies, whose needs will be a focus in each chapter. In Chapter 2 we will look at **Affective Supports**, that is, how a positive classroom environment enhances learning. One cannot talk about English language learners without talking about language development. Chapter 3, **Linguistic Supports**, is designed to provide secondary mathematics teachers, who generally receive little training in teaching reading comprehension and writing, with useful tips for supporting ELLs' language development while still teaching the mathematics course content. Chapter 4 is a look at providing **Cognitive Supports** by teaching mathematics conceptually for long-term acquisition using a variety of strategies, tools, and techniques.

Part II is designed to make the connection between the fundamental support outlined in Part I and real-life classrooms. We will use a ready-made lesson to examine an instructional model that meets the needs of English language learners in Chapter 5, **A 5E Lesson**, and in Chapter 6, we will extend the lesson-planning process one more step by **Adapting a Traditional Textbook Lesson.**

The goal of *Making Math Accessible for English Language Learners* is to provide a tool for teachers to meet the challenge of accelerating English language learners' acquisition of academic English and proficiency in meaningful mathematics.

Chapter 1: *Challenges*

Every student should have equitable and optimal opportunities to learn mathematics free from bias—intentional or unintentional— based on race, gender, socioeconomic status, or language. In order to close the achievement gap, all students need the opportunity to learn challenging mathematics from a well-qualified teacher who will make connections to the background, needs, and cultures of all learners.

NCTM Position Paper, Closing the Achievement Gap, 2005

- Why do some students transition to English very quickly while others attend U. S. schools for many years without acquiring academic English?

- How can we make grade-level mathematics accessible to all students regardless of language proficiency?

- What are the best ways to help students who are not yet proficient in English experience meaningful mathematics?

- What skills do math teachers need to work with English language learners?

Choose a question or set of questions above and respond.

Reflection 1.1 *Speak from your heart, your beliefs, and your past experience.*

You may respond in the space provided.

region **4**
Educated Solutions

Challenges

The rigorous mathematics set forth by the National Council of Teachers of Mathematics (NCTM, 2000) *Principles and Standards for School Mathematics* and required by the Texas Essential Knowledge and Skills (TEKS) demands that educators rethink the teaching of mathematics to make the content accessible to linguistically diverse students. English language learners (ELLs) have traditionally performed at lower levels on standardized tests than other students, even other subgroups, and low language ability makes it difficult to measure mathematics achievement since the test becomes a measure of language as well as content. Additionally, variables such as socioeconomic status, parent education, and family support may outweigh school influences in affecting student achievement. According to Haynes (2003) the problem is compounded because many English language learners have gaps in their mathematics content background due to sporadic attendance or prior education under a curriculum vastly different from that in the United States. Consequently, the ELL gets farther and farther behind his peers when he is denied the opportunity to solve meaningful and challenging problems because of language barriers.

Not only must ELLs learn the mathematics content, but they must do so while learning vocabulary, the structure of the language, and mathematics discourse. Mathematics has it own register, or language specific to mathematics, in which some words have a meaning that is different from the meaning of the commonly-used word, such as *slope* and *leg*. Greek and Latin are the basis of many words, for example, exponent and hypotenuse. Combinations of common words sometimes form mathematical terms, such as *composite number*, *place value*, and *least common denominator*, in which the meaning of the combination of words is different from the sum of the separate definitions. Mathematics texts and word problems are conceptually packed, requiring vertical, horizontal, and, sometimes, diagonal

reading. The student must adjust his reading speed to comprehend technical language containing symbols, which often means he must read the text or problem multiple times (Bye, 1975). However, just because the student is not proficient in English does not mean he cannot think. Delaying the English language learner's participation in true problem solving until he has mastered the English language is not an option. Listening, reading, speaking, and writing skills are the vehicles for understanding, participating in, and communicating mathematical concepts and skills and must be taught concurrently with the mathematics (Crandall, 1985).

In order to provide appropriate instruction to an English language learner that enables him to succeed in rigorous mathematics, it is helpful to understand the process of language acquisition. The chart on the next page can be used to visualize the journey of the English language learner toward abstract and academically challenging mathematics.

According to Cummins (1981), without ELL instructional strategies English language learners generally take four to ten years to become academically proficient in English. They usually go through a silent period of two to five months and spend the first couple of years learning **Basic Interpersonal Communication Skills (BICS)**, that is, learning language related to survival skills, from peers, television, and in other informal settings. During this early stage of development students require the use of concrete-imbedded contexts in the classroom. It often takes another four to seven years for them to comfortably to understand, process, and communicate using academic language and abstract concepts, defined as **Cognitive Academic Language Proficiency (CALP)**, if ELL instructional strategies are not used.

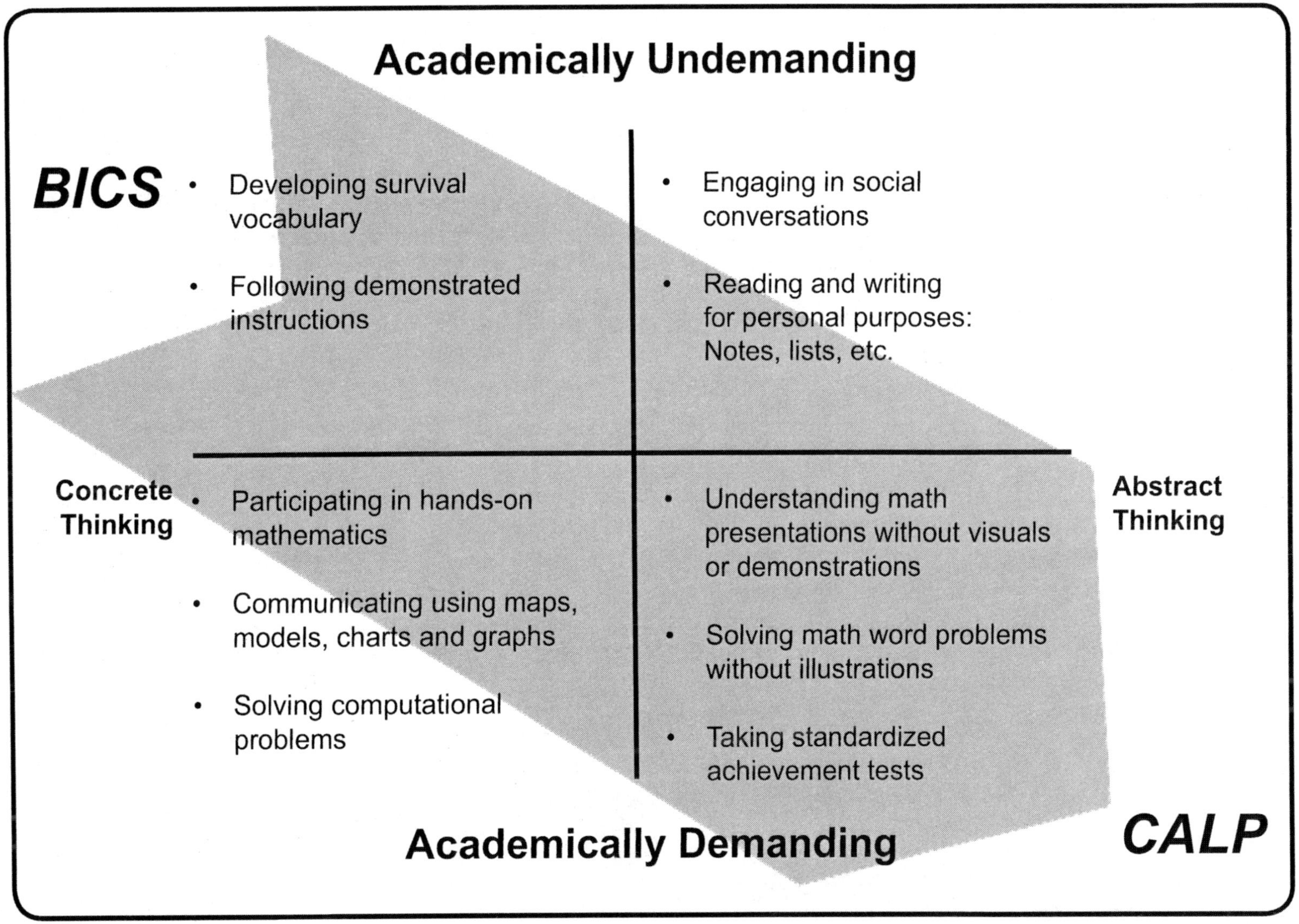

Academically Undemanding

BICS

- Developing survival vocabulary

- Following demonstrated instructions

- Engaging in social conversations

- Reading and writing for personal purposes: Notes, lists, etc.

Concrete Thinking

- Participating in hands-on mathematics

- Communicating using maps, models, charts and graphs

- Solving computational problems

- Understanding math presentations without visuals or demonstrations

- Solving math word problems without illustrations

- Taking standardized achievement tests

Abstract Thinking

Academically Demanding

CALP

Adapted from Cummins (1981).

7

Challenges

Challenges

*B*ICS are usually learned in context-embedded situations such as talking with someone face-to-face or watching the teacher for non-verbal clues in which the student receives immediate feedback. In contrast, CALP generally occurs in a context-reduced setting in which there are few clues to support comprehension. Students usually progress to an advanced level of academically undemanding English much more rapidly than to a level of demanding academic English. It is not unusual to encounter students who are quite proficient in social English while still performing at a very basic level in the language of mathematics.

As you will recall from the Introduction, unless students are under the Special Education umbrella, their mathematics proficiency is assessed with the **Texas Assessment of Knowledge and Skills (TAKS)** in grades 3 through 11 (Exit). However, if an English language learner is classified **Limited English Proficient (LEP)**, reading and English Language Arts (ELA) proficiency is measured using the **Texas English Language Proficiency Assessment System (TELPAS)**. TELPAS is comprised of a series of observation protocols (K-12) used to determine listening, speaking, and writing ratings, and K-2 reading ratings. For Grades 3-12, the reading proficiency rating is determined by the **Reading Proficiency Test in English (RPTE)**. The English language proficiency ratings are:

BEGINNING - This rating indicates the initial stages of learning English and minimal ability to communicate in English.

INTERMEDIATE - This rating indicates the ability to use common, basic English in routine classroom activities.

ADVANCED - This rating indicates the ability to use academic English in classroom activities as long as the necessary English-language assistance is provided.

ADVANCED HIGH - This rating indicates the ability to use academic English in classroom activities with minimal English-language assistance. (TEA, 2004b)

We will use the terms Beginning, Intermediate, Advanced, and Advanced High to describe students' language proficiency, although you may sometimes hear other terminology, such as Early Production instead of Beginning or Fluent instead of Advanced High.

Throughout the book, we will use the descriptors **Understanding, Participating/Processing**, and **Communicating** to organize students' interactions with information. Students must first understand any information they are given. Then they participate with a partner, small groups, the whole class, and/or the teacher as they process the information. Then they communicate by speaking and writing or by non-verbal means such as pointing, choosing, or drawing. Classroom indicators of English language proficiency levels are summarized in the chart on the next page.

TASK 1.1 *Please refer to the case studies that follow the Classroom Indicators chart. Read each case study, review the student's work, and use the Classroom Indicators chart to help you place the student according to English proficiency level on the scale below each case study.*

region *4*
Educated Solutions

Classroom Indicators

	Encouraging Understanding	Encouraging Participating/Processing	Encouraging Communicating
Beginning	• Students often go through a silent period of 2 to 5 months. • Listens but responds in non-verbal ways. • Math text is incomprehensible with the exception of numerals and perhaps a few words linked to the student's background • Facial expressions and body language are indicators of understanding. • Understands less than 1000 words.	• Can actively participate in group hands-on activities. • May "best guess" relationships among numbers in word problems based on past experience in the primary language. • May mimic language without understanding what he is saying. • May procedurally solve math problems without understanding the concept.	• Speaks little if any in English. • Uses "survival" English when attempting to speak English. • Language errors are few because attempts to speak English are very limited.

Intermediate	• Solves simple word problems but still has difficulty with multi-step problems and problems at a high reading level, especially with a lengthy text.
	• Can follow familiar social conversation.
	• Understands less than 7000 words.
		• Is more comfortable working with a partner or small group than in whole-class setting.
		• Can take a more active role in group activities.
		• Begins to process simple problems independently.
			• Uses basic, "simple" English.
			• Speaks and writes using short phrases and sentences.
			• Language errors:
			  ◦ Pronunciation
			  ◦ Grammar
			  ◦ Word order
			• Justifies answers with charts, graphs, tables, and drawings.

Advanced	• May still have difficulty following conversations with pronouns.
	• Understands high-frequency math words.
	• Conditional structure of many word problems is confusing.
	• Comprehends conversation.
	• Understands less than 12,000 words.
		• Participates in social conversation without a great deal of contextual support.
		• Functions moderately at an academic level.
		• Develops increasing proficiency in solving word problems.
		• Can assist other ELLs in cooperative groups.
		• Can lead groups in activities.
		• Comprehends conversation and can engage in student-to-teacher discourse.
			• Uses wider range of vocabulary.
			• Language errors:
			  ◦ Less frequent
			  ◦ Primarily of a complex nature
			  ◦ May continue to misuse/misinterpret passive voice and conditional tense.
			• Can engage in student-to-student discourse.
			• Justifies answers using complete sentences.

Advanced High	• Has advanced cognitive skills and effectively understands academic language. • Understands more than 12,000 words.	• Participates in two-way conversations using academic English. • Functions on grade level with peers.	• Uses enriched vocabulary with few grammatical errors. • May still find passive and conditional tenses difficult. • Uses correct grammar, spelling, and formal mathematics vocabulary to justify answers. • Has advanced cognitive skills and effectively uses academic language.

The Classroom Indicators chart is not a formal TELPAS observation protocol. It is intended as an informal assessment for the classroom teacher to approximate proficiency levels of English language learners, regardless of whether they are classified LEP.

Challenges

Case Study 1

Phong and her parents are immigrants from Vietnam. Phong is a shy sophomore from a family that places a high value on education. She learns quickly but still relies on LEP-modified texts in English and history classes. She becomes frustrated when working contextual problems, especially when given more than two or three word problems to solve.

Phong

Ardene and Gerald made a sketch of a patio and surrounding flowerbed they would like to add to their back yard. The area has outside measurements of 16 feet by 20 feet, and 221 ft^2 of the area is the patio. If the width of the flowerbed is uniform on all sides, find its width, x. Justify your solution.

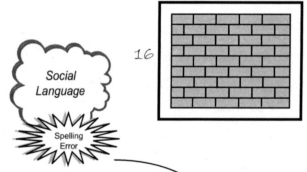

16

Social Language

Spelling Error

Conceptual Error

$16 \times 20 = 320$

$320 - 221 = 99$

The patio has 221 sqaure feet. The whole thing 320 ft. subtract and get 99. Take square root and get about 10 ft. width.

Beginning   **Intermediate**   **Advanced**   **Advanced High**

region 4
Educated Solutions

Case Study 2

Randy, an 11th grader, moved to the United States last fall from Trinidad, where he attended a private school. He lives with his older brother, a university professor. The idioms and slang Randy's friends use occasionally confuse him, but he communicates easily in both social and academic situations and readily learns abstract concepts in his Algebra II class.

Randy

Ardene and Gerald made a sketch of a patio and surrounding flowerbed they would like to add to their back yard. The area has outside measurements of 16 feet by 20 feet, and 221 ft² of the area is the patio. If the width of the flowerbed is uniform on all sides, find its width, x. Justify your solution.

Student checked work.

20

16

Academic Language

Let x = the width of the flowerbed.
Since the width of the flowerbed is x, and there is one on each side of the patio, set up and solve the problem:

13   17

$(16-2x)(20-2x) = 221$

$320 - 32x - 40x + 4x^2 = 221$

$$\frac{-221}{4x^2 - 72x + 99} = 0$$

$$x = \frac{72 \pm \sqrt{5184 - 4(4)(99)}}{2(4)}$$

Communication of mathematical understanding

$x = 72 \pm \sqrt{3600}$ [SIC]

$x = \dfrac{72 \pm 60}{8} = 1.5 \text{ or } 16.5$

16.5 ft. is not a reasonable width for the flowerbed. Therefore, the width is 1.5 feet, which is verified by checking.

← **Beginning**   **Intermediate**   **Advanced**   **Advanced High** →

11

Challenges

Case Study 3

Favian was born in South Texas. His mother does not speak English. She prefers that the family communicate in Spanish when at home. Favian and his friends usually speak Spanish but understand and can speak English well. In class he relies heavily on prior knowledge and has difficulty applying critical thinking skills and using academic English.

Favian

Ardene and Gerald made a sketch of a patio and surrounding flowerbed they would like to add to their back yard. The area has outside measurements of 16 feet by 20 feet, and 221 ft² of the area is the patio. If the width of the flowerbed is uniform on all sides, find its width, *x*. Justify your solution.

Conceptual Error

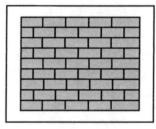

No evidence of understanding academic language

16 x 20 outside
221 ft² inside

(16 x 20) - 221 = 0
320 - 221 = 99 ft of flowers

← Beginning   Intermediate   Advanced   Advanced High →

region 4
Educated Solutions

Case Study 4

Belkiz, who is 18 years old, and her family came to the United States from Pakistan two years ago. The family is active in the Pakistani community, and Belkiz enjoys visiting with her family and many friends. She frequently is absent from school, and when in class, relies on pictures, gestures and translations by her bilingual friends.

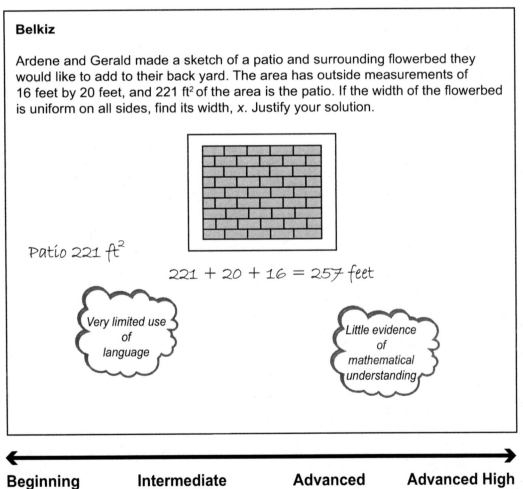

Belkiz

Ardene and Gerald made a sketch of a patio and surrounding flowerbed they would like to add to their back yard. The area has outside measurements of 16 feet by 20 feet, and 221 ft² of the area is the patio. If the width of the flowerbed is uniform on all sides, find its width, *x*. Justify your solution.

Patio 221 ft²

221 + 20 + 16 = 257 feet

Very limited use of language

Little evidence of mathematical understanding

Beginning   Intermediate   Advanced   Advanced High

Challenges

Case Study 5

Rocio, a senior this year, came to the United States from Ecuador three years ago after traveling for several months through Central America and Mexico. She can read unmodified texts with some assistance. She communicates easily, using some descriptive language. She can usually communicate abstract ideas in math class, especially when working with a cooperative group, and plans to go to college next year.

Rocio

Ardene and Gerald made a sketch of a patio and surrounding flowerbed they would like to add to their back yard. The area has outside measurements of 16 feet by 20 feet, and 221 ft² of the area is the patio. If the width of the flowerbed is uniform on all sides, find its width, x. Justify your solution.

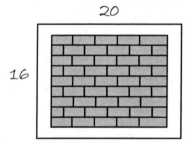

20

16

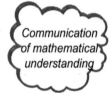

Communication of mathematical understanding

$(16-2x)(20-2x) = 221$

$320 - 32x - 40x + 4x^2 = 221$

$4x^2 - 72x + 99 = 0$

$x = \dfrac{72 \pm \sqrt{-72^2 - 4 \cdot 4 \cdot 99}}{2(4)}$

$x = 72 \pm \overline{)3600}$ [SIC]

$\dfrac{72 \pm 60}{8}$

$x = 16.5$

$x = 1.5$

Width of the flowerbed is 16.5 or 1.5 ft.

← Beginning   Intermediate   Advanced   Advanced High →

region 4
Educated Solutions

Reflection 1.2 *Reflect on some of your present or former students who are English language learners.*

Respond in the chart below.

- *Write the first name of a student beside the level that most accurately describes the student. If possible, identify a student for each level.*

- *What do you think the student perceived as a particularly difficult challenge in your class?*
- *What was your greatest challenge as the student's teacher?*

	Student	Challenge for Student	Challenge for Teacher
Beginning			
Intermediate			
Advanced			
Advanced High			

As you will recall, it generally takes four to ten years in U. S. schools for English language learners to achieve academic English fluency without ELL support (Cummins, 1981). There is simply not enough time between arrival as an English language learner and graduation to wait for students to become fluent in English before engaging them in rigorous mathematics. As Kessler (1985) expressed, our challenge as mathematics educators is to develop mathematical proficiency while the student is still acquiring a second language: English.

Challenges

Big Ideas

- English language learners are not required to be proficient in English prior to being placed in regular math classes.

- English language learners generally become proficient in social language much more rapidly than in academically demanding language.

- Students should be given opportunities to engage in rigorous mathematics, even though their English proficiency may be at a beginning level.

- By learning about the student's background, observing the student's work, and, when possible, finding the student's TELPAS score, the teacher can determine reasonable expectations and plan for appropriate understanding, participation, and communication strategies.

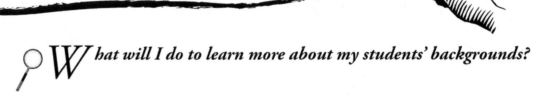

Points to Ponder

What will I do to learn more about my students' backgrounds?

Do I have high expectations for all my students?

What strategies can I use that will support their reaching those expectations?

region 4
Educated Solutions

Challenges

region *4*
Educated Solutions

Chapter 2: *Affective Supports*

*T*here are hundreds of languages in the world, but a smile speaks them all.

--Anonymous

*I*magine you are a student in a classroom surrounded by other students and a teacher, none of whom speak your language.

The English language learner's first impression of the classroom and the teacher set the tone for learning and success. Putting yourself in the place of the student and envisioning what would make you feel welcome will put you on the right path.

The National Council of Teachers of Mathematics (2000) has articulated the importance of a positive classroom climate in learning mathematics. The classroom environment communicates subtle messages about what is valued in learning and doing mathematics and encourages students to participate in the learning and doing of mathematics.

In meeting the affective needs of English language learners, it is important to create a classroom that provides a warm and encouraging atmosphere. An inviting classroom provides the opportunity for learning as well as a way to help students feel relaxed and at home. When students do not understand, they will

Reflection 2.1 *In the space provided, list 3 things that would help make you feel a valued part of the class.*

1. _____

2. _____

3. _____

look around the classroom; so creating an attractive classroom with objects that are both informative and interesting will set the stage for learning.

We all like to be called by our names and to have our names pronounced correctly. Ask the student to say his or her name. Then repeat it back to the student. It is important to read the student's face to see if you said it correctly because many English language learners will hesitate to correct you since correcting adults is considered rude in most cultures. Face the class and use eye contact when speaking to the class so ELL's can use facial expressions and watch your mouth as you form the words to accelerate learning. When using an overhead projector or computer projection device, leaving on some light lets ELLs still watch your face and gestures for visual clues about what you are saying.

Using established routines will also accelerate learning. Students should know, for example, they are to sharpen pencils before the bell rings and immediately have out homework to check and turn in while the teacher silently checks roll and returns homework from the previous day. Teaching routines such as "Raise your hand," and "Move to groups," using the same words each time, empowers even Beginning ELLs so they can quickly learn phrases that allow them to participate with more confidence. There is efficiency and safety in knowing what to expect each day.

English language learners bring with them many strengths. Making opportunities for them to share and participate will benefit all students.

Those who bring sunshine into the lives of others, cannot keep it from themselves.
- James M. Barrie

Hot Tip!

We remember kindnesses shown to us. Create a memory for your students.

Affective Strategies			
Proficiency Level	**Understanding**	**Participating/Processing**	**Communicating**
Beginning **Intermediate** **Advanced** **Advanced High**	• SMILE. • Pronounce the student's name correctly. • Be sure the student knows your name. • Face the class when speaking. • Speak slowly and distinctly. • Repeat important information. • Allow students to tape record lessons. • Label objects in the classroom (Examples: trash, overhead projector). • Create attractive, content-related bulletin boards. • Provide plenty of wait time. • Be patient, kind, understanding, and friendly. • Use all 5 senses.	• SMILE. • Create a positive, non-threatening classroom environment. • Create a nurturing environment. • Find opportunities to bring the student's culture and language into class. • Use frequent, genuine praise. • Establish routines so students know what to expect. • Post procedures and schedules. • Use flexible grouping. • Assign bilingual students as peer partners. • Have groups present work on chart paper. • Highlight contributions of mathematicians from all cultures. • Be patient, kind, understanding, and friendly.	• SMILE. • Be patient, kind, understanding, and friendly. • Provide plenty of wait time. • Create word walls. • Use dry erase boards (can be easily cut from bathroom tile board). • Ask for thumbs up/thumbs down or other physical responses.

Affective Supports

Which of these strategies do you use naturally? **Reflection 2.2**

Which do you make a conscious effort to use?

Which will you add to your repertoire?

1. _____

2. _____

3. _____

TASK 2.1 *Let's revisit the case studies from Chapter 1. Thinking about the affective domain, which of the practices in the previous table would you "play to" with each of the students in the case studies? You may use the space provided beside each case study for your responses.*

region 4
Educated Solutions

Case Study 1

Phong and her parents are immigrants from Vietnam. Phong is a shy sophomore from a family that places a high value on education. She learns quickly but still relies on LEP-modified texts in English and history classes. She becomes frustrated when working contextual problems, especially when given more than two or three word problems to solve.

Phong

Ardene and Gerald made a sketch of a patio and surrounding flowerbed they would like to add to their back yard. The area has outside measurements of 16 feet by 20 feet, and 221 ft^2 of the area is the patio. If the width of the flowerbed is uniform on all sides, find its width, x. Justify your solution.

16

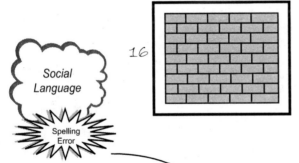

Social Language

Spelling Error

Conceptual Error

$16 \times 20 = 320$

$320 - 221 = 99$

The patio has 221 sqaure feet. The whole thing 320 ft. subtract and get 99. Take square root and get about 10 ft. width.

Beginning ——— Intermediate ——— Advanced ——— Advanced High

Affective Supports

Affective Supports

Case Study 2

Randy, an 11th grader, moved to the United States last fall from Trinidad, where he attended a private school. He lives with his older brother, a university professor. The idioms and slang Randy's friends use occasionally confuse him, but he communicates easily in both social and academic situations and readily learns abstract concepts in his Algebra II class.

Randy

Ardene and Gerald made a sketch of a patio and surrounding flowerbed they would like to add to their back yard. The area has outside measurements of 16 feet by 20 feet, and 221 ft² of the area is the patio. If the width of the flowerbed is uniform on all sides, find its width, x. Justify your solution.

Student checked work.

20

16

Academic Language

Let x = the width of the flowerbed.
Since the width of the flowerbed is x, and there is one on each side of the patio, set up and solve the problem:

$$
\begin{array}{cc}
13 & 17
\end{array}
$$

$$(16 - 2x)(20 - 2x) = 221$$

$$320 - 32x - 40x + 4x^2 = 221$$

$$\dfrac{-221}{4x^2 - 72x + 99} = 0$$

$$x = \dfrac{72 \pm \sqrt{5184 - 4(4)(99)}}{2(4)}$$

Communication of mathematical understanding

$$x = 72 \pm \sqrt{3600} \text{ [SIC]}$$

$$x = \dfrac{72 \pm 60}{8} = 1.5 \text{ or } 16.5$$

16.5 ft. is not a reasonable width for the flowerbed. Therefore, the width is 1.5 feet, which is verified by checking.

Beginning   **Intermediate**   **Advanced**   **Advanced High**

region 4
Educated Solutions

Case Study 3

Favian was born in South Texas. His mother does not speak English. She prefers that the family communicate in Spanish when at home. Favian and his friends usually speak Spanish but understand and can speak English well. In class he relies heavily on prior knowledge and has difficulty applying critical thinking skills and using academic English.

Favian

Ardene and Gerald made a sketch of a patio and surrounding flowerbed they would like to add to their back yard. The area has outside measurements of 16 feet by 20 feet, and 221 ft² of the area is the patio. If the width of the flowerbed is uniform on all sides, find its width, *x*. Justify your solution.

Conceptual Error

No evidence of understanding academic language

16 x 20 outside
221 ft² inside

(16 x 20) - 221 = 0
320 - 221 = 99 ft of flowers

Beginning ⟷ Intermediate ⟷ Advanced ⟷ Advanced High

Affective Supports

Case Study 4

Belkiz, who is 18 years old, and her family came to the United States from Pakistan two years ago. The family is active in the Pakistani community, and Belkiz enjoys visiting with her family and many friends. She frequently is absent from school, and when in class, relies on pictures, gestures and translations by her bilingual friends.

Belkiz

Ardene and Gerald made a sketch of a patio and surrounding flowerbed they would like to add to their back yard. The area has outside measurements of 16 feet by 20 feet, and 221 ft² of the area is the patio. If the width of the flowerbed is uniform on all sides, find its width, *x*. Justify your solution.

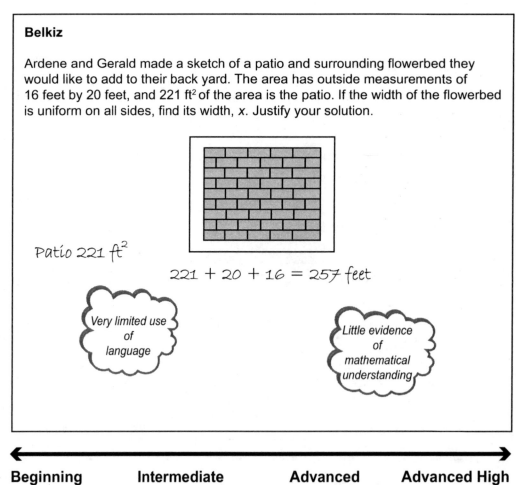

Patio 221 ft²

$$221 + 20 + 16 = 257 \text{ feet}$$

Very limited use of language

Little evidence of mathematical understanding

Beginning   Intermediate   Advanced   Advanced High

Case Study 5

Rocio, a senior this year, came to the United States from Ecuador three years ago after traveling for several months through Central America and Mexico. She can read unmodified texts with some assistance. She communicates easily, using some descriptive language. She can usually communicate abstract ideas in math class, especially when working with a cooperative group, and plans to go to college next year.

Rocio

Ardene and Gerald made a sketch of a patio and surrounding flowerbed they would like to add to their back yard. The area has outside measurements of 16 feet by 20 feet, and 221 ft² of the area is the patio. If the width of the flowerbed is uniform on all sides, find its width, *x*. Justify your solution.

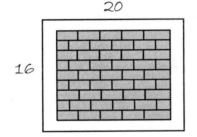

20

16

Communication of mathematical understanding

$(16-2x)(20-2x) = 221$

$320 - 32x - 40x + 4x^2 = 221$

$4x^2 - 72x + 99 = 0$

$x = \dfrac{72 \pm \sqrt{-72^2 - 4 \cdot 4 \cdot 99}}{2(4)}$

$x = 72 \pm \sqrt{3600}$ [SIC]

$\dfrac{72 \pm 60}{8}$

$x = 16.5$

$x = 1.5$

Width of the flowerbed is 16.5 or 1.5 ft.

⟵——————————————————————————⟶

Beginning   **Intermediate**   **Advanced**   **Advanced High**

Affective Supports

Factors Affecting Second Language Acquisition

According to Schumann (1978) how quickly an ELL becomes proficient in English and mathematics is influenced by many factors. Among them are:

Motivation

The degree to which a student wants to, or has a sense of urgency to learn the language is an important factor in determining the rate of language acquisition. The family's priorities concerning language, learning, and school influence the student's desire to become language and content proficient. When there is a large community that speaks the primary language, parents and their children may see little practical need to acquire English. Teachers, counselors, and student mentors can provide opportunities for students to understand the doors that open to those who are fluent in English.

Age

Children who learn a language at a very young age are able to do so naturally and with great ease and efficiency. High school students who are not fluent are at risk of dropping out since they must learn the language and content at a time in their lives when the optimal years for learning a language have passed. They have a short period of time to demonstrate proficiency in both language and the various contents in order to graduate.

Access to the language

When a language other than English is spoken at home and among friends, the contact hours in English are reduced, meaning the student has less opportunity to practice the language. If, in addition, students are removed from the opportunity to interact with other students in class, the problem is compounded.

Personality

Many students have a fairly large receptive vocabulary but are limited in their ability to converse because they lack practice. Extroverts make friends and interact with classmates easily, while the introvert often remains alone unless drawn out by others. Those tendencies directly affect language acquisition. Teachers can provide venues for conversation by providing opportunities for students to work with a partner or small group.

First language development

Some English language learners have not had the opportunity to become proficient in their primary language. They may not have been enrolled in any school for months or possibly years. They may have attended school only sporadically and may not have learned to read or write on grade level. Their exposure to the content areas may be limited. In some countries, mathematics is still taught procedurally and involves little contextual problem solving. Students may enter U. S. classrooms able to compute well but with little conceptual understanding of mathematics.

Cognitive ability

Students come to us with varying levels of innate intelligence. It is the charge of all educators to reach all students effectively, regardless of the ability of the student. English language learners are under-identified as qualifying for special education services because learning disabilities are often dismissed as language deficiencies.

Effective instruction

Effective instruction in both language and content is a major factor in accelerating the student's proficiency. Krashen (1982) asserts that providing comprehensible input through a low affective filter is the most important variable in becoming proficient in both language and content. Effective instruction is evident when students are participating, when information is clearly communicated, and when students' understanding can be seen in their work.

> *Children are like wet cement. Whatever falls on them makes an impression.*
>
> - Dr. Haim Ginott

Affective Supports

Affective Practices and Second Language Acquisition	Motivation	Age	Access to Language	Personality	First Language	Cognitive Ability	Effective Instruction
• SMILE							
• Pronounce the student's name correctly.							
• Be sure the student knows your name.							
• Face the class when speaking.							
• Speak slowly and distinctly.							
• Avoid slang and explain idioms.							
• Repeat important information in exactly the same words.							
• Allow tape recordings of lessons.							
• Label objects in the classroom (Examples: trash, overhead projector).							
• Create attractive content-related bulletin boards.							
• Provide plenty of wait time.							
• Be patient, kind, understanding, and friendly.							
• Utilize all 5 senses.							
• Create a positive, non-threatening classroom environment.							
• Find opportunities to bring the student's culture and language into class.							
• Use frequent, genuine praise.							
• Establish routines so students know what to expect.							
• Post procedures and schedules.							
• Use flexible grouping.							
• Assign bilingual students as peer partners.							
• Have groups present work on chart paper.							
• Highlight contributions of mathematicians from all cultures.							
• Create word walls							
• Use dry erase boards (can be easily cut from bathroom tile board).							
• Ask for thumbs up/thumbs down or other physical responses.							

Affective Supports

TASK 2.2 *Refer to the chart on the previous page, Affective Practices and Second Language Acquisition. Go to the first practice, SMILE. Place a check under each language acquisition factor (motivation, age. . .) that could be influenced by a SMILE. While a SMILE might affect motivation, it cannot influence age. Perhaps it could even have a very small effect on personality, but not on access to language, first language development, or cognitive ability. A SMILE can, however, impact the effectiveness of instruction. Continue to place checks to indicate your responses for each practice.*

Reflection 2.3

Over which of the factors do you have no control?

Over which of the factors do you have some control?

Over which of the factors do you have the greatest control?

region *4*
Educated Solutions

Big Ideas

English language learners benefit from a classroom environment that encourages understanding, participating, and communicating using practices that instill confidence, build self-assurance, and demonstrate respect for heritage.

Some of the factors that influence second language acquisition are:

Motivation	First language development
Age	Cognitive ability
Access to the language	Effectiveness of instruction
Personality	

Providing quality classroom interaction is the factor most within teacher control.

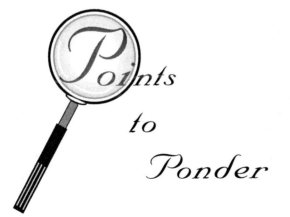

Points to Ponder

What affective supports are available for English learners in your school?

What new affective supports can you use to enhance the effectiveness of instruction?

Notes

Chapter 3: *Linguistic Supports*

*M*athematics knows no race or geographic boundaries; for mathematics, the cultural world is one country.

--David Hilbert

*T*he following example is what a **Beginning** level student might read. Take a moment to try to solve the problem, thinking about what you can determine from the information given. Then do the same with the problem for each level that follows.

A ____ ____ ____ ____ ____ the ____ __ ____ _____ .
The ____ ____ ___ the _____ _____ __ 20 cm. ____ __ __ ____ _____ ___ a
____ __ 4 cm, and the _____ __ a _____ of 43 cm.

The __ ____ _____ __ the ____ ____ _____ __ the ____ and ___ a _____ ___ 51 cm.

The ____ _____ __ the ____ __ the ____ ____ _____ __ the ____ two and a _____ __67 cm.

____ _____ __ the _____ __ ___ __ the ____ _____?

*A*bit frustrating, isn't it? The student can decipher only a few words and pick out the numbers. Even if the student has the mathematics background in his primary language, he does not have enough information to solve the problem.

The following is what an ELL at the **Intermediate** level might read.

A _____ company _____ _____ _____ __ the _____ __ _____ _____ .
The longer _____ ___ the smallest _____ is 20 cm. _____ leg __ ____ _____ ___ a
length __ 4 cm, and the _____ ___ a _____ of 43 cm.

The next larger _____ ___ the same _____ lengths __ the first and ___ a _____ ___ 51 cm.

The third _____ __ the _____ ___ the same ____ lengths __ the other two and a _____ of 67 cm.

What _____ ___ the length __ each leg __ the third _____?

Even though students at the **Intermediate** level probably have acquired an active social vocabulary, they still do not possess the mathematics vocabulary or understanding of the abstract structure of the language in problems such as the example above to reach the solution without significant support.

$\mathcal{T}$he following is what an **Advanced** level student might read.

A tile company manufactures _____ tiles in the shape _____ isosceles trapezoids. The longer base ____ the smallest trapezoid is 20 cm. Each leg __ this trapezoid has a length __ 4 cm, and the trapezoid has a perimeter __ 43 cm.

The next larger trapezoid has the same base lengths __ the first and has a perimeter ____ 51 cm.

The third trapezoid __ the _____ has the same base lengths __ the other two and a perimeter __ 67 cm.

What _____ be the length of each leg __ the third trapezoid?

At the **Advanced** level, students are proficient enough in both English and the language of mathematics to solve the problem with some ELL support since they may continue to have difficulty with prepositions, pronouns, conditional tense and/or passive voice. An example of conditional tense is: *If* Johnny has one penny one day and doubles that amount each day thereafter, how much money *would* he have on the 31st day?

An example of active voice versus passive voice is:
    Active Voice: Johnny hit the ball.
    Passive Voice: The ball was hit by Johnny.
Students may frequently struggle with reversals between English and equations: A number x is 5 less than y, is written $x = y - 5$. ELLs often will write $x = 5 - y$.

Linguistic Supports

W̱e would expect students at the **Advanced High** level of language proficiency to read problems on grade level with few, if any, LEP modifications. The following is the original problem.

A tile company manufactures decorative tiles in the shape of isosceles trapezoids. The longer base of the smallest trapezoid is 20 cm. Each leg of this trapezoid has a length of 4 cm, and the trapezoid has a perimeter of 43 cm.

The next larger trapezoid has the same base lengths as the first and has a perimeter of 51 cm.

The third trapezoid in the series has the same base lengths as the other two and a perimeter of 67 cm.

What would be the length of each leg of the third trapezoid?

You may use this space to solve the problem. The answer appears below.

Answer: 16 cm.

Linguistic Obstacles

Students conversing readily with other students is not necessarily an indicator they are fluent in academic English. Being proficient in social situations is very different from being fluent in the language of mathematics. Look for clues by comparing written work, spoken responses, and conversational language. Even when the student is at the Advanced level of proficiency in the language of mathematics and the content of the course, the number of steps required to solve the problem creates a challenge. In Texas students are required to solve multi-step problems at the Apply, Analyze, and Evaluate levels of Bloom's Taxonomy in order to meet high school graduation requirements. Such problems present many challenges to the English language learner. The length of the text is also a factor in students' persistence. If the text is too long, he will likely give up.

Common meanings for words such as *base* (as in the bottom of an object) and *leg* (as in the limb of an animal) may confuse ELLs in mathematical contexts. Distinguishing between the bases and legs is academic vocabulary that, although the student may know in his primary language, he may not be able to apply unless he is able to connect the words to concepts he already understands. Connections are made when the vocabulary is actively taught, defined in a modified text, or discovered while participating in activities.

Mathematics texts contain more concepts per word, sentence, and paragraph than any other kind of text. Authors of mathematics texts generally write in a very terse or compact style. Each sentence contains a large amount of compressed information, with little redundancy. Unlike reading a passage in a novel or even a social studies textbook, students find it difficult to determine meaning when solving math problems by using the surrounding context. Instead, the math student must construct meaning by making connections between the new information and his or her prior knowledge about the topic. The stronger and more varied the background a reader has in terms of knowledge and skills, the faster he will learn and be able to apply what he reads (Barton and Heidema, 2002).

Is Reading Math Hard?

A gin functions to process cotton at x cubic yards a minute. What function describes the gin's function?

A company builds tables with proportional tops so the tables nest. Create a table to represent the proportional measurements of the tables.

Linguistic Supports

Example 1

The table below shows how much Andy earns for working a certain number of hours.

Number of Hours	Earnings
16	$120.00
18	$135.00
20	$150.00
22	$165.00
h	

How much does Andy earn per hour? Write an equation that could be used to determine Andy's earning (E) for working h hours.

Answer: $7.50; E=7.5h

The assumption is that Andy's earnings over the last 4 weeks are tied to the number of hours and earnings in the table. To process the information, reading from left to right and then moving to the next line is not sufficient. In order to find the pattern, it is necessary to read vertically to find the rate of change of earning versus hours. That is, for every 2 more hours he works, he earns $15 more.

Example 2

Determine the slope of the line graphed below.

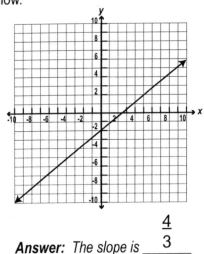

Answer: The slope is $\dfrac{4}{3}$

Example 3

The hood ornament for a new luxury automobile is shown below. $\overline{RU}$ is a diameter, $m\widehat{UV}= 40°$, $m\widehat{QV} = 100°$ and $m\widehat{QR}= m\widehat{RS}$.

Find $m\angle QVR$ and $m\angle RTS$

Example 4

Joan is planning to make a special cylinder to hold a present she bought for her sister. She would like to construct it of lightweight cardboard and use tape to seal the edges. Therefore, there will be no overlapping of the material. If the diameter of the cylinder is to be 10 inches and the height 11 inches, find the amount of cardboard needed to make the container, disregarding any waste. (Use 3.14 for π).

Answer: 502.4 in²

Educated Solutions

Linguistic Supports

*T*he preceding examples demonstrate the unique knowledge and skills required to read mathematics that are not taught in other content areas. Students must be able to read left to right, right to left, top to bottom, bottom to top. (*See Example 1.*) In some cases, they must even find the information diagonally. (*See Example 2.*)

Mathematics requires students to be proficient at decoding not only words but also numeric and non-numeric symbols and graphics. *(See Example 3.)*

Technical terminology and abstractions, multiple meanings of words used in everyday language and mathematics, and the use of synonyms in the same problem pose additional challenges for English language learners and their math teachers. *(See Example 4.)*

Concepts are frequently embedded in other concepts (Barton and Heidema, 2002). Still referring to Example 4, for students to conceptually understand finding the total surface area of a cylinder as opposed to plugging values into a formula, they must first understand that the net created by a cylinder is comprised of two congruent circles and a rectangle. The length of the rectangle is actually the circumference of the circles, and the width of the rectangle is the height of the cylinder. When they understand the net created by the cylinder, they can understand why they must find the areas of the circles that comprise the top and bottom, which they will add to the area of the rectangle. The formula then makes sense:

$A = \pi r^2 + \pi r^2 + (2\pi rh)$

$A = 2\pi r^2 + 2\pi rh$ or $A = 2\pi r (r + h)$ if simplified by factoring out $2\pi r$.

Examine again the trapezoid problem. (See next page.) Highlight features of the problem that make it difficult for ELLs at each level of language proficiency.

TASK  **3.1**

Linguistic Supports

Beginning

A tile company manufactures decorative tiles in the shape of isosceles trapezoids. The longer base of the smallest trapezoid is 20 cm. Each leg of this trapezoid has a length of 4 cm, and the trapezoid has a perimeter of 43 cm.

The next larger trapezoid has the same base lengths as the first and has a perimeter of 51 cm.

The third trapezoid in the series has the same base lengths as the other two and a perimeter of 67 cm.

What would be the length of each leg of the third trapezoid?

Intermediate

A tile company manufactures decorative tiles in the shape of isosceles trapezoids. The longer base of the smallest trapezoid is 20 cm. Each leg of this trapezoid has a length of 4 cm, and the trapezoid has a perimeter of 43 cm.

The next larger trapezoid has the same base lengths as the first and has a perimeter of 51 cm.

The third trapezoid in the series has the same base lengths as the other two and a perimeter of 67 cm.

What would be the length of each leg of the third trapezoid?

Advanced

A tile company manufactures decorative tiles in the shape of isosceles trapezoids. The longer base of the smallest trapezoid is 20 cm. Each leg of this trapezoid has a length of 4 cm, and the trapezoid has a perimeter of 43 cm.

The next larger trapezoid has the same base lengths as the first and has a perimeter of 51 cm.

The third trapezoid in the series has the same base lengths as the other two and a perimeter of 67 cm.

What would be the length of each leg of the third trapezoid?

Advanced High

A tile company manufactures decorative tiles in the shape of isosceles trapezoids. The longer base of the smallest trapezoid is 20 cm. Each leg of this trapezoid has a length of 4 cm, and the trapezoid has a perimeter of 43 cm.

The next larger trapezoid has the same base lengths as the first and has a perimeter of 51 cm.

The third trapezoid in the series has the same base lengths as the other two and a perimeter of 67 cm.

What would be the length of each leg of the third trapezoid?

Overcoming Linguistic Obstacles

*I*f students are to become fluent in the language of mathematics, teachers must guide and support the reading process (Barton & Heidema, 2002). They must equip students with strategies to understand mathematical text at the same time the students are learning math concepts.

Early Beginning ELLs go through a silent period. ELLs with teachers sensitive to this silent period who make the effort to provide opportunities for non-verbal communication will be rewarded with students that progress beyond the silent period quickly. Picture dictionaries, bilingual dictionaries, tape recorders, and videos are valuable classroom resources that allow ELLs to use and reinforce visual, written, and auditory modalities for learning English. Picture dictionaries and bilingual dictionaries foster independence since the ELL can find meanings of words and concepts without having to ask the teacher or another student, and tape recordings and videos let the student replay teacher lessons or lessons from other sources as many times as necessary.

Another option for Beginning students is the lesson preview in which the content teacher, ESL teacher, or a paraprofessional provides the student with a summary of the lesson. This is not a translation. If a teacher or paraprofessional translates the lesson, the student will quickly learn to tune out the English and rely on the translation. Working with the ESL teacher so math vocabulary and, if possible, math content can be part of the ESL class provides an additional opportunity for language and content practice as well as the opportunity to learn from a teacher who may provide a different approach to learning. English Language Arts teachers can also help by incorporating essential non-math vocabulary into their lessons, and many are eager to help students develop the different meanings of words in non-academic and mathematical contexts.

The students' continued progress is dependent on providing supports appropriate to their proficiency level. If English language learners are to have the same opportunities to succeed as their peers, acquiring English language and mathematics proficiency must be intertwined. Notice in the table on the next page that understanding, participating, and communicating involve both English and the language of mathematics. Although mathematics content is embedded throughout, the focus in this chapter is on language support.

Some strategies that can enhance student learning are compiled in the charts on the next two pages.

Education, beyond all other devices of human origin, is the great equalizer of the conditions of man, – the balance-wheel of the social machinery.

- Horace Mann

Linguistic Practices		
Proficiency Level	**Understanding**	**Participating/Processing**	**Communicating**

Proficiency Level	Understanding	Participating/Processing	Communicating

Beginning	☐ Let the tone of your voice and body language show your students you enjoy teaching.
	
	☐ Speak slowly. (Louder does not make it easier to understand.)
	
	☐ Enunciate clearly. Avoid "gonna, "gotta," and "lotsa."
	
	☐ Avoid slang and idioms.
	
	☐ Simplify your spoken language.
	
	☐ Emphasize nouns and verbs with your voice while speaking.
	
	☐ Demonstrate what you are talking about.
	
	☐ Use pictures for clarification.
	
	☐ Repeat frequently using the same sentences to allow students time to translate.
	
	☐ Provide wait time. Remember it takes longer to process in a second language.
	
	☐ Write legibly.
	
	☐ Print is easier to read than cursive.
	
	☐ Use sans-serif fonts, such as Arial instead of serif fonts, such as Times New Roman.
	
	☐ Provide visuals.
	
	☐ Teach comparison words: more, less, most, least, greater than, equal, half as much, twice as many.
	
	☐ Teach mathematics vocabulary using tools such as vocabulary concept maps and word walls.
	
	☐ Post key vocabulary.
	
	☐ If the resources are available, provide pre-lessons in the student's primary language.
		☐ Create a learning center or section on a bookshelf that might include:
		
		   ☐ Picture dictionary
		
		   ☐ Illustrated math dictionary
		
		   ☐ Bilingual dictionary
		
		   ☐ Native language textbook
		
		☐ Have ELL work with a partner or in small groups of students, including students who are not ELL.
		
		☐ Have student groups produce collaborative work to share with other groups and/or the class.
		
		☐ Incorporate manipulatives and real-life objects into lessons.
		
		☐ Provide activities that allow the student to draw, match, circle, choose, point, or act out.
		
		☐ If possible, provide translations of textbooks and assignments.
		
		☐ Simplify the language and highlight important words on assignments.
			☐ Learn to read students' expressions for clues to determine whether they understand.
			
			☐ Provide opportunities for the student to respond by drawing, matching, circling, choosing, pointing, acting, and demonstrating.
			
			☐ Accept visual representations from the students (charts, graphs).

Linguistic Supports

Linguistic Strategies			
Proficiency Level	**Understanding**	**Participating/Processing**	**Communicating**
Intermediate	☐ *Continue to use the strategies listed above as needed and:* ☐ Encourage ELLs to use illustrated mathematics dictionaries. ☐ Teach special mathematical meanings for words commonly used in English (e.g. point, base, lateral). ☐ Rewrite word problems in simpler language, using illustrations when possible. ☐ Teach content vocabulary using word matches with cognates and vocabulary concept maps. ☐ Provide partially-completed notes with sketches.	☐ *Continue to use the strategies listed above as needed and:* ☐ Design lessons that relate to the students' backgrounds and prior knowledge. ☐ Tie lessons to students' interests. ☐ Provide activities that allow students to list, label, identify, and answer in short strings of words. ☐ Provide word banks with activities. ☐ Have students prepare their own glossaries of mathematical terms. ☐ Allow ELL to tape record lessons and replay as needed to help with assignments.	☐ *Continue to use the strategies listed above as needed and:* ☐ Structure questions that allow the student to respond in a way appropriate to the proficiency of the student. ☐ Provide opportunities for the student to respond by listing, labeling, identifying, and answering in short strings of words. ☐ Encourage students to use student-generated glossaries and word banks. ☐ Do not penalize the student for mistakes in grammar and pronunciation.
Advanced	☐ *Continue to use the strategies listed above as needed and:* ☐ Continue to use LEP-adapted materials as needed.	☐ *Continue to use the strategies listed above as needed and:* ☐ Provide opportunities for student-teacher and student-student dialogue. ☐ Provide opportunities for students to describe, define, explain, compare, contrast, and justify. ☐ Have students write word problems (in groups).	☐ *Continue to use the strategies listed above as needed and:* ☐ Encourage students to write using complete sentences with more academic language. ☐ Utilize journals. ☐ Provide opportunities for students to speak using longer and more complex phrases and sentences. ☐ Provide opportunities for students to respond by describing, defining, explaining, comparing and contrasting, and justifying.
Advanced High	☐ *Continue to use the strategies listed above as needed and:* ☐ Provide opportunities to work with more complex text. ☐ Provide opportunities for understanding differences in intonation between the primary language and English.	☐ *Continue to use the strategies listed above as needed and:* ☐ Provide opportunities for leadership. ☐ Design activities that require higher levels of language and mathematics.	☐ *Continue to use the strategies listed above as needed and:* ☐ Expect students to write complex sentences using correct grammar, spelling, and academic language. ☐ Students should demonstrate well-developed metacognitive skills.

Linguistic Supports

region 4
Educated Solutions

Reflection 3.1

On the Language Practices chart on the preceding pages, check the box for each strategy you already use. Review the remaining strategies in the Linguistic Practices chart. Choose a strategy or set of strategies you think would be effective to use with your ELL students.

1. *Why did you select the strategy or strategies?*
2. *What can you do to incorporate the strategy or strategies in your classroom?*
3. *What is a challenge you may encounter in implementing the strategy or strategies, and how might you overcome the challenge?*

1. _____

_____

_____

2. _____

_____

3. _____

_____

Linguistic Supports

The strategies you reflected on can be utilized to enhance the learning experience of students on a daily basis. Consideration should also be given to prior knowledge and background in an effort to increase the students knowledge and background for continued studies in mathematics. Prior knowledge and background affect how easily new knowledge and skills are acquired. In addition, prior knowledge must also be accessible in long-term memory. When teachers help students learn to organize similar concepts and terminology and facilitate their understanding of the relationship between them, the information becomes accessible in long-term memory (Barton & Heidema, 2002). Learning has occurred when new knowledge can be retrieved from long-term memory.

Building Vocabulary

Graphic representations enhance student memory. In fact, representations such as graphic organizers and concept maps are more effective learning tools for mathematics concepts than colorful pictures and photographs (Imhof, et al, 1996, cited in Barton & Heidema, 2002). One such organizer is a **concept definition map**, also known as a webbing. Concept definition maps are useful to help students connect concepts and supporting vocabulary. Another graphic organizer that relies heavily on the use of visual representations and connections to the student's background is a **vocabulary organizer**. The example on the next page is a combination of the Frayer model (Frayer, Frederick, and Klausmeier, 1969, cited in Barton & Heidema, 2002) and the Verbal and Visual Word Association (VVWA) (Readence, Bean, and Baldwin, 2001, cited in Barton & Heidema, 2002) strategies.

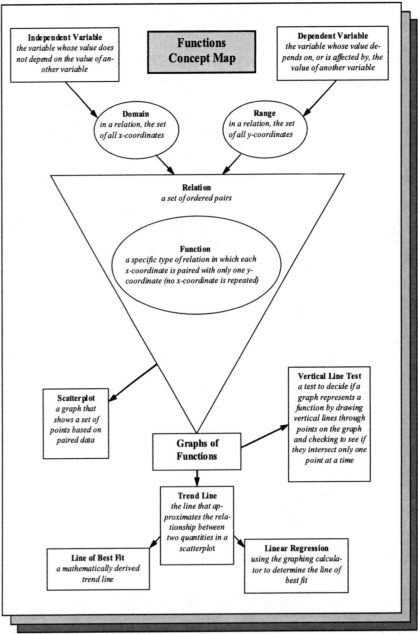

Concept Definition Map

Used with permission. (Region 4 Education Service Center, 2005)

Vocabulary Organizer

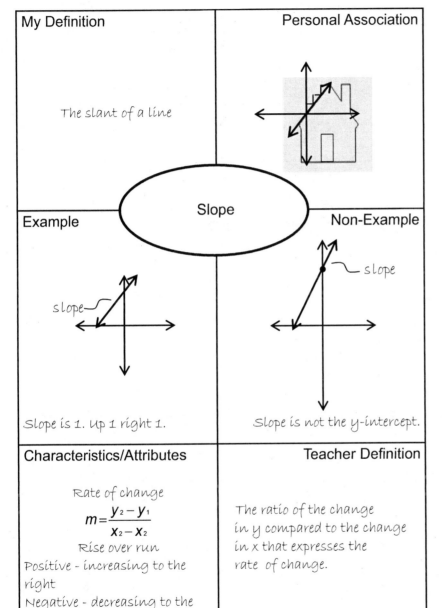

My Definition	Personal Association
The slant of a line	
Example	**Non-Example**
Slope is 1. Up 1 right 1.	Slope is not the y-intercept.
Characteristics/Attributes	**Teacher Definition**

Characteristics/Attributes:

Rate of change

$$m = \frac{y_2 - y_1}{x_2 - x_2}$$

Rise over run

Positive - increasing to the right

Negative - decreasing to the right.

Teacher Definition:

The ratio of the change in y compared to the change in x that expresses the rate of change.

Think-Alouds

*I*t is important to introduce concept definition maps and vocabulary organizers with teacher **think-alouds**. The teacher verbalizes her thought process in developing the concept definition map or vocabulary organizer. Including non-examples is critical because it is often the most obvious indicator of any student misconceptions. When students first begin using a vocabulary concept definition map, they will need help in choosing meaningful mathematical examples and non-examples. For instance, drawing a tree is not an appropriate non-example in the case of slope since a tree has no meaningful characteristics in common with slope. A meaningful non-example possesses characteristics that can be compared to and contrasted with the term or concept being developed. In the non-example to the right, it is clear the student understands the slope is not the *y*-intercept.

After the think-aloud, students can begin developing their own concept definition maps in their groups using chart paper with the teacher facilitating. When the work is posted, it provides the opportunity for students to examine other groups' efforts and enrich their thinking as a result. Working together as a group and sharing the work product allows English language learners the opportunity to participate actively in learning vocabulary and concepts.

Hot Tip!

Prompt groups to create concept definition maps and/or vocabulary organizers on chart paper to post as a word wall.

Linguistic Supports

47

Hot Tip!

Have students begin a new concept definition map when a concept is introduced. Then as the concept is expanded, they can add more details to the map.

TASK 3.2 *Decide on a mathematics vocabulary word and use the vocabulary organizer template to the right to develop it.*

region *4*
Educated Solutions

Linguistic Supports

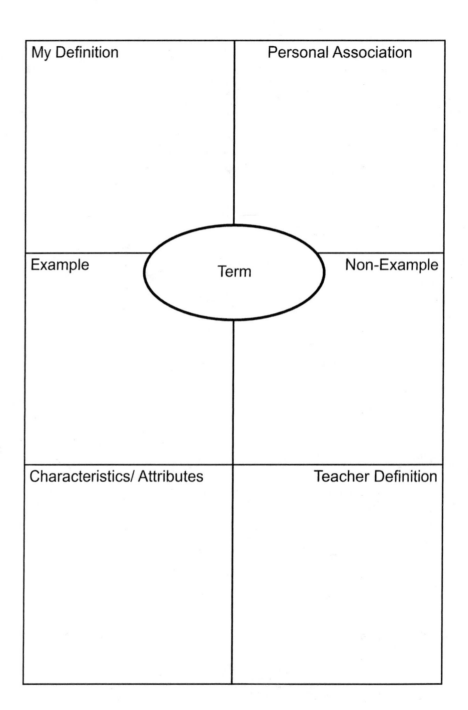

My Definition	Personal Association
Example	Term	Non-Example
Characteristics/ Attributes	Teacher Definition

Cognates

*L*earning cognates, words that are closely related to words in the student's primary language, is especially helpful to Spanish-speaking students and others for whom the primary language is rooted in Latin, and to a lesser extent, Greek.

Examples: **formas forms**   **variedad variety**   **equivalente equivalent**

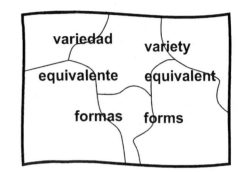

(See Appendix for a list of some common English-Spanish math cognates.)

Sample activities:

> formas   forms

Sentence strips and puzzles are useful tools in helping students recognize similarities in language.

Word Sorts

*I*f students can categorize words, there is a good chance they comprehend. Word sorts are activities that help students learn to organize concepts mentally. You can provide a bank of words and prompt students to sort the words into categories. Allow students to define their own categories, using questioning strategies only as necessary when they are having difficulty.

Sample sort:

Word Bank: angle, circle, line, plane, polyhedron, prism, pyramid, ray, rectangle, sphere, square, triangle

One Dimension	Two Dimensions	Three Dimensions
line	angle	polyhedron
ray	circle	prism
	plane	pyramid
	rectangle	sphere
	square	
	triangle	

Linguistic Supports

Find Someone Who

Instructions: Find someone who can explain one of the following words. Ask him or her to write the definition, draw the representation, and then sign his or her name. You may not use the same person for more than one word.

WORD	DEFINITION	PICTURE	SIGNATURE
Circle			
Chord			
Circumference			
Radius			
Diameter			
Central Angle			

TASK 3.3 *Refer to the case studies again. Determine which linguistic strategies and possible activities you would use to encourage understanding, participating, and communicating. Use the space provided beside each case study to respond.*

Linguistic Supports

50  region 4
Educated Solutions

Case Study 1

Phong and her parents are immigrants from Vietnam. Phong is a shy sophomore from a family that places a high value on education. She learns quickly but still relies on LEP-modified texts in English and history classes. She becomes frustrated when working contextual problems, especially when given more than two or three word problems to solve.

Phong

Ardene and Gerald made a sketch of a patio and surrounding flowerbed they would like to add to their back yard. The area has outside measurements of 16 feet by 20 feet, and 221 ft² of the area is the patio. If the width of the flowerbed is uniform on all sides, find its width, x. Justify your solution.

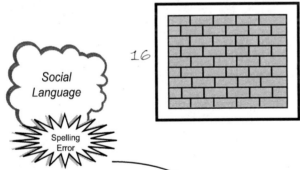

16

Conceptual Error

Social Language

Spelling Error

$16 \times 20 = 320$

$320 - 221 = 99$

The patio has 221 sqaure feet. The whole thing 320 ft. subtract and get 99. Take square root and get about 10 ft. width.

Beginning   Intermediate   Advanced   Advanced High

Linguistic Supports

Case Study 2

Randy, an 11th grader, moved to the United States last fall from Trinidad, where he attended a private school. He lives with his older brother, a university professor. The idioms and slang Randy's friends use occasionally confuse him, but he communicates easily in both social and academic situations and readily learns abstract concepts in his Algebra II class.

Randy

Ardene and Gerald made a sketch of a patio and surrounding flowerbed they would like to add to their back yard. The area has outside measurements of 16 feet by 20 feet, and 221 ft² of the area is the patio. If the width of the flowerbed is uniform on all sides, find its width, x. Justify your solution.

Student checked work.

20

16

Academic Language

Let x = the width of the flowerbed.
Since the width of the flowerbed is x, and there is one on each side of the patio, set up and solve the problem:

$$\underset{13}{(16-2x)} \underset{17}{(20-2x)} = 221$$

$$320 - 32x - 40x + 4x^2 = 221$$

$$\frac{-221}{4x^2 - 72x + 99} = 0$$

$$x = \frac{72 \pm \sqrt{5184 - 4(4)(99)}}{2(4)}$$

$$x = 72 \pm \sqrt{3600} \ [\text{SIC}]$$

$$x = \frac{72 \pm 60}{8} = 1.5 \text{ or } 16.5$$

Communication of mathematical understanding

16.5 ft. is not a reasonable width for the flowerbed. Therefore, the width is 1.5 feet, which is verified by checking.

Beginning   Intermediate   Advanced   Advanced High

Case Study 3

Favian was born in South Texas. His mother does not speak English. She prefers that the family communicates in Spanish when at home. Favian and his friends usually speak Spanish but understand and can speak English well. In class he relies heavily on prior knowledge and has difficulty applying critical thinking skills and using academic English.

Favian

Ardene and Gerald made a sketch of a patio and surrounding flowerbed they would like to add to their back yard. The area has outside measurements of 16 feet by 20 feet, and 221 ft² of the area is the patio. If the width of the flowerbed is uniform on all sides, find its width, *x*. Justify your solution.

Conceptual Error

No evidence of understanding academic language

16 x 20 outside
221 ft² inside

(16 x 20) - 221 = 0
320 - 221 = 99 ft of flowers

Beginning   **Intermediate**   **Advanced**   **Advanced High**

Linguistic Supports

Case Study 4

Belkiz, who is 18 years old, and her family came to the United States from Pakistan two years ago. The family is active in the Pakistani community, and Belkiz enjoys visiting with her family and many friends. She frequently is absent from school, and when in class, relies on pictures, gestures and translations by her bilingual friends.

Belkiz

Ardene and Gerald made a sketch of a patio and surrounding flowerbed they would like to add to their back yard. The area has outside measurements of 16 feet by 20 feet, and 221 ft² of the area is the patio. If the width of the flowerbed is uniform on all sides, find its width, *x*. Justify your solution.

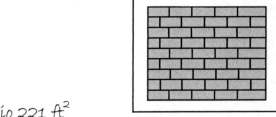

Patio 221 ft²

221 + 20 + 16 = 257 feet

Very limited use of language

Little evidence of mathematical understanding

Beginning　　　Intermediate　　　Advanced　　　Advanced High

Linguistic Supports

region 4
Educated Solutions

Case Study 5

Rocio, a senior this year, came to the United States from Ecuador three years ago after traveling for several months through Central America and Mexico. She can read unmodified texts with some assistance. She communicates easily, using some descriptive language. She can usually communicate abstract ideas in math class, especially when working with a cooperative group, and plans to go to college next year.

Rocio
Ardene and Gerald made a sketch of a patio and surrounding flowerbed they would like to add to their back yard. The area has outside measurements of 16 feet by 20 feet, and 221 ft^2 of the area is the patio. If the width of the flowerbed is uniform on all sides, find its width, *x*. Justify your solution.

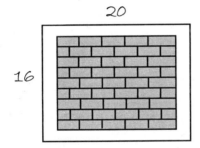

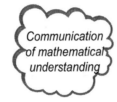

Communication of mathematical understanding

$$(16-2x)(20-2x) = 221$$
$$320 - 32x - 40x + 4x^2 = 221$$
$$4x^2 - 72x + 99 = 0$$

$$x = \frac{72 \pm \sqrt{-72^2 - 4 \cdot 4 \cdot 99}}{2(4)}$$

$$x = 72 \pm \sqrt{3600} \text{ [SIC]}$$

$$\frac{72 \pm 60}{8}$$

$$x = 16.5$$
$$x = 1.5$$

Width of the flowerbed is 16.5 or 1.5 ft.

Beginning   Intermediate   Advanced   Advanced High

Linguistic Supports

Reflection 3.2 *How might you use the activities discussed in this chapter in your classroom?*

region *4*
Educated Solutions

- Mathematics text is more compact than other texts and requires unique knowledge and skills not taught in other areas.

- The syntax of word problems, including pronouns, prepositions, reversals, conditional tense, and passive voice makes understanding more difficult.

- Abstractions, multiple meanings, and embedded concepts also make understanding the language of mathematics difficult.

- The student's background, prior knowledge, and primary language development influence the rate at which he will become proficient in English and mathematics.

- Cognates can be useful in helping Spanish-speaking students understand they know more English than they thought since there are so many similarities between English and Spanish.

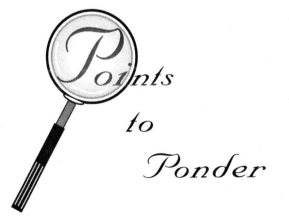

How do I know my English language learners understand?

Are my English language learners actively engaged in learning, regardless of language proficiency?

Am I providing a variety of modalities to encourage communication at the highest level the ELL is capable of producing?

Linguistic Supports

57

region 4
Educated Solutions

Chapter 4: *Cognitive Supports*

The true spirit of delight, the exaltation, the sense of being more than Man, which is the touchstone of the highest excellence, is to be found in mathematics as surely as in poetry"

- Bertrand Russell

In Chapter 2, "Affective Supports," we looked at the classroom environment as an influence on language acquisition and mathematical learning. Since the factor over which educators have the most control is the quality of instruction, we will continue to emphasize the importance of reaching all students as we look at understanding, participating, and communicating mathematical concepts in much the same way we looked at "Linguistic Supports" in Chapter 3. However, the emphasis in this chapter is on supporting the development of the skills, conceptual understanding, and thought processes that lead to mathematical proficiency.

When students encounter a word problem, they must not only read the text but also decode the mathematics involved. They must determine relevant concepts, including whether there is extraneous information, and decide which operations to use on any numbers.

TASK 4.1

You will recall the problem presented in Chapter 3. Study each sample on the following pages to determine what mathematical concepts the student will be able to identify about the problem. Do you think the student could solve the problem? Justify your response.

 region *4*
Educated Solutions

Cognitive Supports

Beginning

A _____ _____ _____ _____ _____ _____ _____ __ the _____ __ _____ _____ _____.
The _____ _____ ___ the _____ _____ _____ 20 cm. _____ ___ __ _ _____ _____ ___ a
_____ __ 4 cm, and the _____ ___ a _____ of 43 cm.

The ___ _____ _____ ___ the ____ _____ ___ the _____ and ___ a _____ ___ 51 cm.

The ____ _____ __ the _____ ___ the _____ _____ _____ __ the ____ two and a _____ of 67 cm.

_____ _____ ___ the _____ __ ____ __ the _____ _____?

Could a **Beginning** level student solve this problem? Why or Why not? What mathematical concepts could he/she determine at this level of proficiency?

Cognitive Supports

Intermediate

A _____ company _____ _____ _____ ____ the _____ __ _____ _____.
The longer _____ _____ the smallest _____ is 20 cm. _____ leg __ _____ _____ has a
length of 4 cm, and the _____ has a _____ of 43 cm.

The next larger _____ has the same _____ lengths ___ the first and has a _____ _____ 51 cm.

The third _____ in the _____ has the same _____ lengths ___ the other two and a _____ of 67 cm.

What _____ _____ the length ___ each leg ___ the third _____?

Could a **Intermediate** level student solve this problem? Why or Why not? What mathematical concepts could he/she determine at this level of proficiency?

Cognitive Supports

Advanced

A brick company manufactures _____ bricks in the shape _____ isosceles trapezoids. The longer base ____ the smallest trapezoid is 20 cm. Each leg __ this trapezoid has a length of 4 cm, and the trapezoid has a perimeter of 43 cm.

The next larger trapezoid has the same base lengths __ the first and has a perimeter ___ 51 cm.

The third trapezoid in the _____ has the same base lengths __ the other two and a _____ of 67 cm.

What _____ be the length of each leg of the third trapezoid?

Could an **Advanced** level student solve this problem? Why or Why not? What mathematical concepts could he/she determine at this level of proficiency?

region 4
Educated Solutions

Cognitive Supports

Original Problem

A brick company manufactures decorative bricks in the shape of isosceles trapezoids. The longer base of the smallest trapezoid is 20 cm. Each leg of this trapezoid has a length of 4 cm, and the trapezoid has a perimeter of 43 cm.

The next larger trapezoid has the same base lengths as the first and has a perimeter of 51 cm.

The third trapezoid in the series has the same base lengths as the other two and a perimeter of 67 cm.

What would be the length of each leg of the third trapezoid?

Could an **Advance High** level student solve this problem? Why or Why not? What mathematical concepts could he/she determine at this level of proficiency?

Cognitive Supports

Mathematics Obstacles

*I*n addition to the obstacles English language learners and their teachers face in learning the language of mathematics, many immigrant students come from schools where concepts and skills may have been taught or emphasized differently than in U. S. schools. The following are some examples of those differences:

- Commas and decimal points may be interchanged.
  For example: 248.067.225,53 is the same as 248,067,225.53.

- Numerals may be formed differently.
  It is not infrequent for students to cross the numeral "7," written 7 or "9" written as 9.

It is more problematic when the numerals are vastly different. For instance, "3" is written ٣ and pronounced *thalatha* in Arabic.

- Subtraction may be done by borrowing from the bottom numbers. For example: If you have a place value in the subtrahend (bottom number) greater than the place value in the minuend (top number), subtract the bottom number from 10 and add the result. You have to adjust by adding 1 to the digit to the left. Then subtract.

Step 1: 9 4 -3 8	The digit 8 is greater than the digit above it (8).
Step 2: 10 - 8 = 2	Subtract 8 from 10.
Step 3: 2 + 4 = 6	Add the result (2) to the top digit in the one's place (4).

Step 4: 9 4 -3 8 6	Write the result (6) in the ones place of the answer
Step 5: 9 4 -⁴3 8 5 6	To compensate for using 10 when we subtracted, add 1 to the ten's digit (3) and subtract.

- Divisors and dividends may be expressed differently. For example: In some countries, "a divided by b" is written a : b, whereas in the United States the colon is restricted to expressing ratios. Many students are unfamiliar with the obelus (÷).

- The metric system may be used exclusively, which greatly decreases the need for learning fractions.

- Manipulatives may have not been used.

- Estimation may not have been emphasized.

- Concept development may have been stressed far more than computational skills, or vice versa.

- Geometry is not emphasized in some countries.

It is helpful to be aware that there are differences in prior knowledge, but it is sometimes difficult to determine whether students are struggling with the language or with the concept. We already know that ELLs are not going to volunteer to respond in front of the whole class and risk the embarrassment of not-yet-proficient language, even if they understand the mathematics. So how do we know if they are "getting it?"

One person's constant is another person's variable.
— Susan Gerhart

Cognitive Supports

Reflection 4.1 *In the space provided, describe some of the actions you have observed from English Language learners who don't understand the concept.*

What are some of the ways they compensate for not understanding?

Overcoming Mathematics Obstacles

There are many ways to check for student understanding including non-verbal clues such as body language and facial expressions that indicate, "I got it!" or "I haven't a clue about this." Asking the student to explain his strategies and reasoning in his primary language to a bilingual student who can then translate and help draw the early-level student into the discussion can help the teacher determine whether the student understands the language and concepts. Beginning students can also show they understand by choosing from examples and non-examples. Asking the student to make a sketch, graph, table, chart, or other representation lets him demonstrate understanding non-verbally. As students become more language proficient, other ways to check for understanding include asking them to restate what has already been said by others, asking them to explain their own reasoning, asking if they may have solved the problem a different way, and noticing when they point out something wrong (Secada and de la Cruz, 1996).

When new concepts are introduced or when it is determined the student does not understand a concept, the teacher can draw from strategies that encourage mathematical learning. In the following table, new strategies appropriate to the proficiency level are in bold type.

Cognitive Supports

Mathematics Strategies			
Proficiency Level	**Understanding**	**Participating/Processing**	**Communicating**

Beginning	• Provide meaningful contexts related to the student's background.
	
	• Connect learning to prior knowledge.
	
	• Use comparing and contrasting to accelerate understanding.
	
	• Provide ample wait time.
	
	• Utilize ESL teacher, bilingual aides, parent volunteers, to provide short pre-lessons, not direct translations of the lesson.
	
	• Use and teach students to use tools such as calculators with graphing capabilities.
	
	• Provide simplified notes (with pictures).
		• Encourage students to work together.
		
		• Use manipulatives and visuals to model methods for problem solving.
		
		• Use games that reinforce concepts.
		
		• Assign projects for students to work with a partner or small group.
		
		• Use and teach students to use tools such as calculators with graping capabilities.
		
		• Limit length of assignments.
			• Provide opportunities for students to engage in mathematical discourse even if nonverbal:
			  • Teacher to student
			  • Student to teacher
			  • Student to student
			
			• Allow students to demonstrate knowledge using tables, graphs, charts, and pictures.
			
			• Extend response time.
			
			• Use dry erase boards (can be easily cut from bathroom tileboard).
			
			• Ask for thumbs up/thumbs down responses.
			
			• Make assessments as free from bias as possible.
			
			• Make assessments that measure mathematical understanding, not reading proficiency.
			
			• Assess using alternative methods such as group projects, rubrics, checklists, journals, and portfolios.

Intermediate	• Provide meaningful contexts related to the student's background.
	
	• Connect learning to prior knowledge.
	
	• Use comparing and contrasting to accelerate understanding.
	
	• Provide ample wait time.
	
	• Utilize ESL teacher, bilingual aides, parent volunteers, to provide short pre-lessons, not direct translations of the lesson.
	
	• Use and teach students to use tools such as calculators with graphing capabilities.
	
	• Provide simplified notes with pictures.
	
	• **Modify texts and activities to reflect similar language but do NOT simplify the content.**
	
	• **Ask scaffolding questions.**
	
	• **Include tables, graphs, charts, and drawings to assist students in understanding posed problems.**
	
	• **Use multiple representations in problem solving.**
	
	• **Provide partially-completed study guides.**
		• Encourage students to work together.
		
		• Use manipulatives and visuals to model methods for problem solving.
		
		• Use games that reinforce concepts.
		
		• Assign projects for students to work with a partner or small group.
		
		• Use and teach students to use tools such as calculators with graphig capabilities.
		
		• Limit length of assignments.
		
		• **Provide opportunities for students to think about their thinking: How do you know that? Why did you decide it was not. . .?**
		
		• **Teach test-taking and study skills.**
			• Provide opportunities for students to engage in mathematical discourse even if nonverbal:
			  • Teacher to student
			  • Student to teacher
			  • Student to student
			
			• Allow students to demonstrate knowledge using tables, graphs, charts, and pictures.
			
			• Extend response time.
			
			• Use dry erase boards (can be easily cut from bathroom tileboard).
			
			• Ask for thumbs up/thumbs down responses.
			
			• Make assessments as free from bias as possible.
			
			• Make assessments that measure mathematical understanding, not reading proficiency.
			
			• Assess using alternative methods such as group projects, rubrics, checklists, journals, and portfolios.
			
			• **Emphasize thoughtful, quality responses.**
			
			• **Ask students to justify answers using tables, graphs, drawings, and a few words or short phrases in English.**

Mathematics Strategies			
Proficiency Level	**Understanding**	**Participating/Processing**	**Communicating**

Advanced	• Provide meaningful contexts related to the student's background.
	
	• Connect learning to prior knowledge.
	
	• Use comparing and contrasting to accelerate understanding.
	
	• Provide ample wait time.
	
	• Utilize ESL teacher, bilingual aids and parent volunteers to provide short pre-lessons but not direct translatitons of the lesson.
	
	• Use and teach students to use tools such as calculators with graphing capabilities.
	
	• Provide simplified notes (with pictures).
	
	• Modify texts and activities to reflect similar language but do NOT simplify the content.
	
	• Ask scaffolding questions.
	
	• Include tables, graphs, charts, and drawings to assist students in understanding posed problems.
	
	• Use multiple representations in problem solving.
	
	• Provide partially-completed study guides.
	
	• **Encourage students to develop their own study guides.**
		• Encourage students to work together.
		
		• Use manipulatives and visuals to model for problem solving.
		
		• Use games that reinforce concepts.
		
		• Assign projects for students to work with a partner or small group.
		
		• Use and teach students to use tools such as calculators with graphing capabilities.
		
		• Provide opportunities for students to think about their thinking: How do you know that? Why did you decide it was not. . .?
		
		• Teach test-taking and study skills.
			• Provide opportunities for students to engage in mathematical discourse even if nonverbal:
			  • Teacher to student
			  • Student to teacher
			  • Student to student
			
			• Allow students to demonstrate knowledge using tables, graphs, charts, and pictures.
			
			• Extend response time.
			
			• Use dry erase boards (can be easily cut from bathroom tile board).
			
			• Ask for thumbs up/thumbs down responses.
			
			• Make assessments as free from bias as possible.
			
			• Make assessments that measure mathematical understanding, not reading proficiency.
			
			• Assess using alternative methods such as group projects, rubrics, checklists, journals, and portfolios.
			
			• Emphasize thoughtful, quality responses.
			
			• Ask students to justify answers using tables, graphs, drawings and a few words or short phrases in English.
			
			• **Ask questions that require more lengthy explanations.**
			
			• **Ask questions that require more complex knowledge of the language of mathematics.**
			
			• **Ask students to verify answer in English using complete sentences to explain tables, graphs, drawings, etc.**

Cognitive Supports

Mathematics Strategies			
Proficiency Level	**Understanding**	**Participating/Processing**	**Communicating**

Advanced High	• Modify texts and activities to reflect simpler language, but do not simplify the content.
	
	• Use and teach students to use tools such as calculators with graphing capabilities.
	
	• Use comparing and contrasting to accelerate understanding.
	
	• Provide ample wait time.
	
	• Provide meaningful contexts related to the student's background.
	
	• Connect learning to prior knowledge.
	
	• Ask scaffolding questions.
	
	• Include tables, graphs, charts, and drawings to assist students in understanding posed problems.
	
	• Use multiple representations in problem solving.
	
	• Provide partially-completed notes.
	
	• Encourage students to develop their own study guides.
		• Encourage student involvement.
		
		• Use manipulatives and visuals to model methods for problem solving.
		
		• Use games that reinforce concepts.
		
		• Assign projects for students to work with a partner or small group.
		
		• Use and teach students to use tools such as calculators with graphing capabilities.
		
		• Provide opportunities for students to think about their thinking: How do you know that? Why did you decide it was not. . .?
		
		• Teach test-taking and study skills.
			• Provide opportunities for students to engage in mathematical discourse even if nonverbal:
			  • Teacher to student
			  • Student to teacher
			  • Student to student
			
			• Allow students to demonstrate knowledge using tables, graphs, charts, and pictures.
			
			• Extend response time.
			
			• Use dry erase boards (can be easily cut from bathroom tile board).
			
			• Ask for thumbs up/thumbs down responses.
			
			• Make assessments as free from bias as possible.
			
			• Make assessments that measure mathematical understanding, not reading proficiency.
			
			• Assess using alternative methods such as group projects, rubrics, checklists, journals, and portfolios.
			
			• Emphasize thoughtful, quality responses.
			
			• Ask students to justify answers using tables, graphs, drawings and a few words or short phrases in English.
			
			• Ask questions that require more complex knowledge of language of mathematics.
			
			• Ask students to verify answers in English using sentences to explain tables, graphs, drawings, etc.
			
			• **Prompt students to justify answers using complex sentences with correct grammar, descriptive language, and academic vocabulary.**

Cognitive Supports

Activities for Understanding, Participating/Processing and Communication

The following are some examples of mathematics tools and strategies. Manipulatives such as positive/negative counters to model integers; blocks for building area and volume models and viewing 3-dimensional objects; patty paper for geometry constructions, definitions, and proofs; isometric dot paper; plastic polygons; geoboards; algebra concrete models; and realia (real-life objects used to enhance learning) provide essential connections for all learners, especially ELLs, in developing mathematics proficiency.

Example of blocks and isometric dot paper.

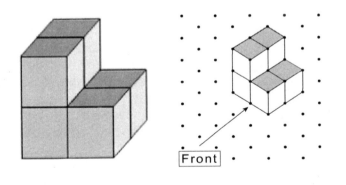

Example of an algebra concrete model.

Use a concrete model to represent the following expression and simplify.

$(3x + 1) + (x - 5) - (2x - 3)$

Distribute the negative (actually -1) over $(2x - 3)$. In the model, you will flip the terms being subtracted:

$(3x + 1) + (x - 5) - (2x - 3) = (3x + 1) + (x - 5) - 2x + 3$

Two zero pairs are formed with x terms and four zero pairs are formed by constant terms and removed.

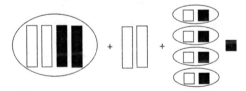

Combine the remaining like terms leaving the following.

$2x - 1$

Cognitive Supports

Example of patty paper, grid paper, and table to teach transformations:

1. Record the vertices of triangle *ABC* in the table.
2. Place the patty paper (tracing paper) over the grid paper.
3. Trace the triangle and the axis. Label the triangle *A′ B′ C′* .
4. Reflect the triangle across the x-axis. Record the vertices of triangle *A′ B′ C′* in the table.

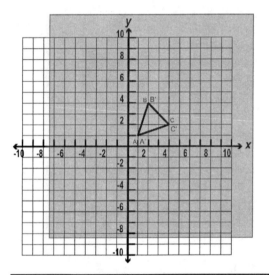 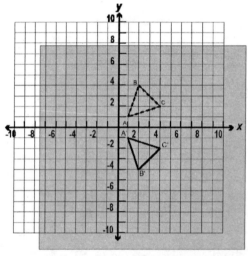

Original Figure	Original Image Reflected Across the *x*-axis
A (1, 1)	A' (1,-1)
B (2, 4)	B' (2, -4)
C (4, 2)	C' (4, -2)
(x, y)	(x, -y)

*T*echnology such as graphing calculators, data collection devices, and computers provides infinite possibilities for students to understand, participate in, and communicate mathematics efficiently with few language limitations. They can readily explore the results of changing the parameters of a function and then immediately see the connection between the tabular, graphical, and algebraic representations of the function. They can collect data with a motion detector in order to explore the effect on a graph of changing velocity. They can collect data from the Internet, display it in a spreadsheet, and use the data to create graphs and charts. Nearly all students enjoy using technology, and the wise teacher uses that to his or her advantage.

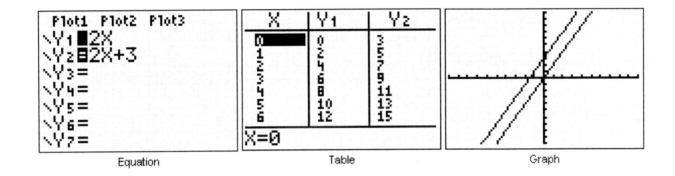

| Equation | Table | Graph |

*C*oncepts can also be reinforced or reviewed using **example/non-example t-charts**. They can serve as an informal assessment. The student completes the table with a list of examples and non-examples supporting the concept in the heading.

Proportions	
Example	*Non-Example*
y-intercept is at the origin.	y-intercept is at (0, 4).
Constant rate of change	1 pencil costs $.15 3 pencils cost $0.35
$y = 2x$	$y = 2x + 3$

*T*he child's game **What Am I?** uses comparing and contrasting to develop understanding of a particular concept. A word bank is an appropriate adaptation for Beginning and Intermediate English language learners. To be most effective with ELLs, the teacher draws a t-chart or table on a transparency or the board, with columns for "yes" and "no." Then she chooses hints such as those below which she will say, write, and, when possible, use gestures to demonstrate.

Yes	No
I have only 1 *y*-value for any 1 *x*-value.	I cannot be a vertical line.
I have an input and resulting output.	
One quantity depends on another quantity.	

The answer is : I am a function.

*C*oncept sorts decrease the need for verbal and/or written language in that the steps need only be arranged in the correct order. They provide a filter to help the student overcome a language deficiency that may interfere with learning a concept. The following flowchart proof is an example. The cut pieces are bagged and distributed to small groups, partners, or individual students to sort. The teacher monitors and corrects any misconceptions.

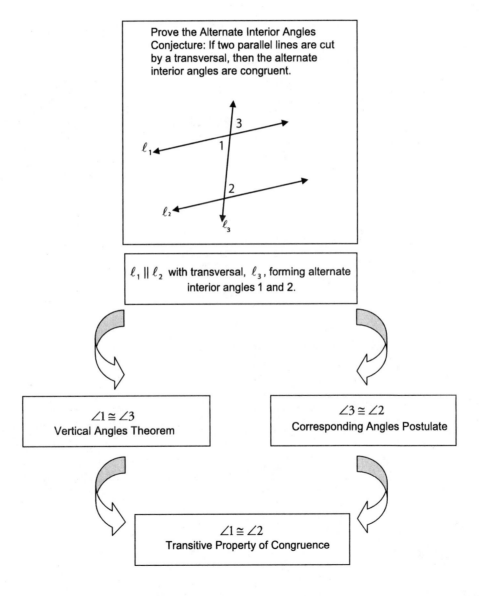

Window panes can be used to explore related concepts. In this case the students are given an equation and asked to fill in each of the panes. As with any organizer, window panes should be phased in with teacher think-alouds and modeling, followed by group work, before individual students are expected to complete the activity independently.

$$4 - y = 3x$$

Slope-Intercept Form	Domain	Table
$4 - y = 3x$ $\underline{\quad -4 \quad -4 \quad}$ $-y = 3x - 4$ $\dfrac{-y}{-1} = \dfrac{3x-4}{-1}$ $y = -3x + 4$	All real numbers **Range** All real numbers	
Slope $m = -3$ The rate of change is –3.	**Y-Intercept** The *y*-intercept is 4. The coordinates of the *y*-intercept are (0, 4)	**Graph**

*I*t is important for students to represent and make connections among equations, tables, graphs, and verbal descriptions of problem situations. In a graphic organizer such as the **4-quadrant problem solver** below, the student is given one of the four representations and fills in the other three. You can further enhance learning by asking students to represent the 4 quadrants on chart paper. After they post their work, the groups can share out during a "gallery tour."

Sample student work

Verbal

The Handel family is considering renting a minivan for their vacation to another state. The cost of the minivan is $45.00 per day plus $0.35 per mile. The drive is an 800 mile round trip, and they plan to be gone 7 days. They decided they would spend no more than $600 renting the minivan. Can they rent the minivan and stay within their budget? Justify your answer.

Table

$x = miles$
$y = cost$

x	Process	y
0	7(45) + 0	315
1	7(45) + .35(1)	315.35
2	315 + .35(2)	315.70
3	315 + .35(3)	316.05
x		315 + .35x

Student realized he could simplify 7(45) to get 315.

Suggest that student add leading zero to .35.

Graph

I used the graphing calculator to show they spend $595 and can do it.

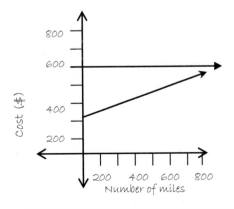

Equation

$y = 315 + .35x$
$y = 315 + .35(800)$
$y = 595$

Multiply 7 x 45 since the minivan is $45 each day plus 800 miles x .35 per mile equals $595. So they have enough money.

Cognitive Supports

While the 4-quadrant problem solver on the previous page lends itself to algebra problems, the **See-Plan-Do-Reflect** model below is appropriate for use with a wide variety of problems. We will use it in Chapter 5.

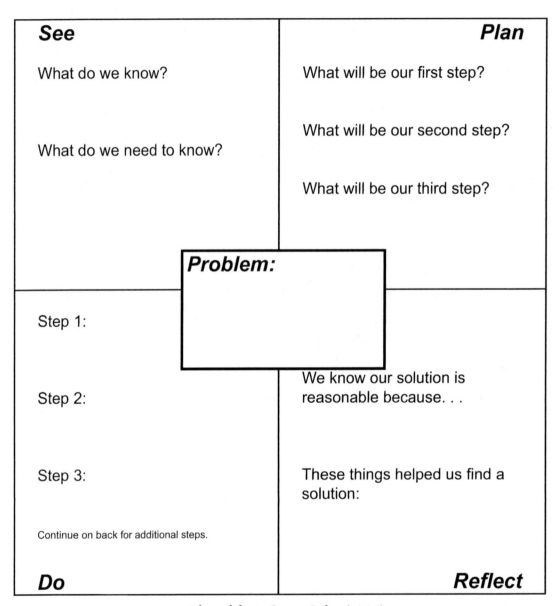

Hot Tip!

As a warm-up or closing activity, present a multi-step problem. Ask students to identify the steps needed to solve the problem, just the steps; do not have ask them to solve the problem. This gives ELLs practice with reading and interpreting problems and will strengthen their language skills without having to worry about solving the problem.

See

What do we know?

What do we need to know?

Plan

What will be our first step?

What will be our second step?

What will be our third step?

Problem:

Do

Step 1:

Step 2:

Step 3:

Continue on back for additional steps.

We know our solution is reasonable because. . .

These things helped us find a solution:

Reflect

Adapted from George Polya (1957)

region 4
Educated Solutions

*I*t is also important to use instructional practices that encourage the student's metacognitive development. Metacognitive practices help students become more aware of their own mental processes during problem solving. That in turn contributes to the classroom becoming an environment of cooperation and inquiry, enhancing all students' abilities to work both independently and interdependently. The following metacognitive activity provides an opportunity for students to compare and contrast their ideas and thought processes with others.

Bonded Brains provides a structure for students to work within and between groups to converse and learn. For example, you arrange the class in groups of 4. Each group works a given problem that has one correct answer but multiple ways of getting to the answer. (See www.mathbenchmarks.org, a free database developed by the Region 4 Education Service Center, for such problems that can be selected by TEKS.) Distribute playing cards, so that no two members of the same group have the same number. After home groups have completed the problem, the teacher prompts the twos to form a new group. The threes form a second new group, and so forth. After the new groups discuss the problem and complete the Bonded Brains activity sheet, they return to their home groups, debrief each other, and make any revisions they would like to their original work.

Bonded Brains

My Group's Ideas	Ideas from Other Groups
	Which ideas did all the groups have in common?
	Which ideas were different?
	What did I learn from members of other groups?

TASK 4.2 *We will again visit the case studies. Consider the work sample and description of each student. Which of the preceding tools and activities would you use with each of the students in the case studies? Would you use the tool or activity to encourage understanding, participating/processing, or communicating? Use the table below to indicate your response.*

Student Name	Student Activity	Manipulatives (specify which)	Technology	What Am I?	Example/ Non-Example	Concept Sorts	Window Panes	Quadrant Problem Solver	See-Plan-Do-Reflect	Bonded Brains
Phong	Understanding									
Phong	Participating									
Phong	Communicating									
Randy	Understanding									
Randy	Participating									
Randy	Communicating									
Favian	Understanding									
Favian	Participating									
Favian	Communicating									
Belkiz	Understanding									
Belkiz	Participating									
Belkiz	Communicating									
Rocio	Understanding									
Rocio	Participating									
Rocio	Communicating									

Case Study 1

Phong and her parents are immigrants from Vietnam. Phong is a shy sophomore from a family that places a high value on education. She learns quickly but still relies on LEP-modified texts in English and history classes. She becomes frustrated when working contextual problems, especially when given more than two or three word problems to solve.

Phong

Ardene and Gerald made a sketch of a patio and surrounding flowerbed they would like to add to their back yard. The area has outside measurements of 16 feet by 20 feet, and 221 ft^2 of the area is the patio. If the width of the flowerbed is uniform on all sides, find its width, x. Justify your solution.

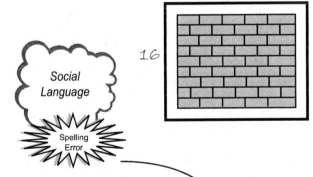

16

Social Language

Spelling Error

Conceptual Error

$16 \times 20 = 320$

$320 - 221 = 99$

The patio has 221 sqaure feet. The whole thing 320 ft. subtract and get 99. Take square root and get about 10 ft. width.

Beginning   Intermediate   Advanced   Advanced High

Cognitive Supports

Case Study 2

Randy, an 11th grader, moved to the United States last fall from Trinidad, where he attended a private school. He lives with his older brother, a university professor. The idioms and slang Randy's friends use occasionally confuse him, but he communicates easily in both social and academic situations and readily learns abstract concepts in his Algebra II class.

Randy

Ardene and Gerald made a sketch of a patio and surrounding flowerbed they would like to add to their back yard. The area has outside measurements of 16 feet by 20 feet, and 221 ft² of the area is the patio. If the width of the flowerbed is uniform on all sides, find its width, x. Justify your solution.

20

16

Student checked work.

Academic Language

Let x = the width of the flowerbed.
Since the width of the flowerbed is x, and there is one on each side of the patio, set up and solve the problem:

$$\begin{array}{cc} 13 & 17 \\ (16-2x) & (20-2x) = 221 \end{array}$$

$$320 - 32x - 40x + 4x^2 = 221$$

$$\frac{-221}{4x^2 - 72x + 99} = 0$$

$$x = \frac{72 \pm \sqrt{5184 - 4(4)(99)}}{2(4)}$$

$$x = 72 \pm \sqrt{3600} \text{ [SIC]}$$

$$x = \frac{72 \pm 60}{8} = 1.5 \text{ or } 16.5$$

Communication of mathematical understanding

16.5 ft. is not a reasonable width for the flowerbed. Therefore, the width is 1.5 feet, which is verified by checking.

←————————————————————————————→

Beginning   **Intermediate**   **Advanced**   **Advanced High**

 region 4
Educated Solutions

Cognitive Supports

Case Study 3

Favian was born in South Texas. His mother does not speak English. She prefers that the family communicates in Spanish when at home. Favian and his friends usually speak Spanish but understand and can speak English well. In class he relies heavily on prior knowledge and has difficulty applying critical thinking skills and using academic English.

Favian

Ardene and Gerald made a sketch of a patio and surrounding flowerbed they would like to add to their back yard. The area has outside measurements of 16 feet by 20 feet, and 221 ft² of the area is the patio. If the width of the flowerbed is uniform on all sides, find its width, *x*. Justify your solution.

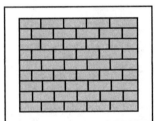

Conceptual Error

No evidence of understanding academic language

16 x 20 outside
221 ft² inside

(16 x 20) - 221 = 0
320 - 221 = 99 ft of flowers

Beginning　　Intermediate　　Advanced　　Advanced High

Cognitive Supports

Case Study 4

Belkiz, who is 18 years old, and her family came to the United States from Pakistan two years ago. The family is active in the Pakistani community, and Belkiz enjoys visiting with her family and many friends. She frequently is absent from school, and when in class, relies on pictures, gestures and translations by her bilingual friends.

Belkiz

Ardene and Gerald made a sketch of a patio and surrounding flowerbed they would like to add to their back yard. The area has outside measurements of 16 feet by 20 feet, and 221 ft² of the area is the patio. If the width of the flowerbed is uniform on all sides, find its width, *x*. Justify your solution.

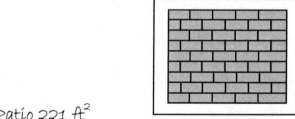

Patio 221 ft²

221 + 20 + 16 = 257 feet

Very limited use of language

Little evidence of mathematical understanding

Beginning   Intermediate   Advanced   Advanced High

Case Study 5

Rocio, a senior this year, came to the United States from Ecuador three years ago after traveling for several months through Central America and Mexico. She can read unmodified texts with some assistance. She communicates easily, using some descriptive language. She can usually communicate abstract ideas in math class, especially when working with a cooperative group, and plans to go to college next year.

Rocio

Ardene and Gerald made a sketch of a patio and surrounding flowerbed they would like to add to their back yard. The area has outside measurements of 16 feet by 20 feet, and 221 ft^2 of the area is the patio. If the width of the flowerbed is uniform on all sides, find its width, *x*. Justify your solution.

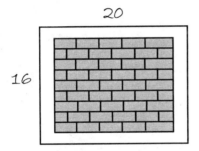

20

16

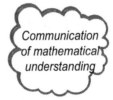

Communication of mathematical understanding

$$(16-2x)(20-2x) = 221$$

$$320 - 32x - 40x + 4x^2 = 221$$

$$4x^2 - 72x + 99 = 0$$

$$x = \frac{72 \pm \sqrt{-72^2 - 4 \cdot 4 \cdot 99}}{2(4)}$$

$$x = 72 \pm \sqrt{3600} \text{ [SIC]}$$

$$\frac{72 \pm 60}{8}$$

$$x = 16.5$$

$$x = 1.5$$

Width of the flowerbed is 16.5 or 1.5 ft.

Beginning   **Intermediate**   **Advanced**   **Advanced High**

83

Cognitive Supports

Reflection 4.2 *Referring to the table in Task 4.2, which strategies, tools, and activities would you use if you had all 5 case study students in the same class?*

Assessment

Assessment can be informal or formal but should be linked to curriculum and instruction, used as an instrument to direct future instruction, and should be as free of bias as possible. Assessment should be authentic and directly reflect student learning (McLaughlin, 1993).

According to McLaughlin, an essential part of authentic assessment is that it applies to real-life situations in which students participate in meaningful tasks. Authentic assessment is frequently multi-dimensional in that it uses more than one piece of evidence, such as the response to a multiple-choice question, to assess student learning. Students are encouraged to exhibit their thought processes through writing and representations such as charts, graphs and tables. A rubric is generally used to ascertain student progress.

The problem in the student case studies is an example of an authentic assessment, or performance assessment, and could be scored using a rubric such as the one on the next page.

Rubric

The rubric on the following page reflects the major component of what it means to be able to know and do mathematics. According to the Texas Essential Knowledge and Skills for all grade levels, National Council of Teachers of Mathematics (2000), and the National Research Council (2002), thinking mathematically encompasses the development of students' conceptual knowledge, procedural knowledge, and ability to communicate mathematically. These are the three criteria on which to provide student instruction and judge student performance.

Conceptual Knowledge

Conceptual knowledge is the knowledge of "what." Students demonstrate their understanding of how different pieces of information are interconnected and interrelated in a systematic way. A proficient student correctly identifies the attributes of the problem that leads them to correct inferences and combines the critical attributes of the problem in order to describe correctly the mathematical relationship(s) inherent in the problem. This criterion aligns with the National Research Council's first proficiency, "Understand," of what it means for anyone to learn mathematics successfully.

Procedural Knowledge

Procedural knowledge is the knowledge of "how." Students demonstrate their understanding of skills, algorithms, techniques, and methods in determining and using strategies to solve the problem. A proficient student correctly selects and implements an appropriate strategy, uses appropriate representation to connect the procedure to the concept of the problem, and correctly implements the procedure to arrive at a correct solution to the problem. This criterion aligns with the National Research Council's second and third proficiency, "Applying and Computing," of what it means for anyone to learn mathematics successfully.

Communication

Communication is the knowledge of "why." Students provide clear, detailed, and organized analysis to justify the solution, using correct terminology and notation. The presentation of the solution clearly demonstrates the thinking process. A proficient student fully answers the question of "why" for the selected strategy, explains the procedure used, and evaluates the solution for reasonableness using age-appropriate terminology and notation. This criterion aligns with the National Research Council's fourth proficiency, "Reasoning," of what it means for anyone to learn mathematics successfully.

The rubric results can be reported using a chart like the one below.

a.	Yes	No	Student arrives at a correct solution?			
			4	3	2	1
b. Conceptual Knowledge						
c. Procedural Knowledge						
d. Communication						

Cognitive Supports

Part a) Correct Solution   Yes   No

Criteria	4	3	2	1
Part b) **Conceptual Knowledge**	**Attribute(s) of concept(s)** Correctly identifies attributes of the problem, which leads to correct inferences. **Inferences** Combines the critical attributes of the problem in order to describe correctly the mathematical relationship(s) inherent in the problem.	**Attribute(s) of concept(s)** Correctly identifies attributes of the problem, which leads to correct inferences. **Inferences** Combines the critical attributes of the problem in order to describe correctly the mathematical relationship(s) inherent in the problem.	**Attribute(s) of concept(s)** Identifies some of the attributes of the problem, which leads to partially correct inferences. **Inferences** Combines the identified attributes of the problem which leads to a partial identification of the mathematical relationship(s) inherent in the problem.	**Attribute(s) of concept(s)** Lacks identification of any of the critical attributes of the problem. **Inferences** Combines few of the attributes of the problem which leads to an incomplete identification of the mathematical relationship(s) inherent in the problem.
Part c) **Procedural Knowledge**	**Appropriate strategy** Selects and implements an appropriate strategy. **Representational form** Uses appropriate representation to connect the procedure to the concept of the problem. **Algorithmic competency** Correctly implements procedure to arrive at a correct solution.	**Appropriate strategy** Selects and implements an appropriate strategy. **Representational form** Uses appropriate representation to connect the procedure to the concept of the problem. **Algorithmic competency** Implements selected procedure but arrives at an incorrect solution.	**Appropriate strategy** Selects and implements an appropriate strategy. **Representational form** Uses inconsistent or insufficient representation for the selected solution strategy. **Algorithmic competency** Implements selected procedure but arrives at an incorrect or correct solution. (See Part a above)	**Appropriate strategy** Selects and implements an inappropriate strategy. **Representational form** Uses incorrect representations. **Algorithmic competency** Makes significant errors.
Part d) **Communication**	**Justification** Fully answers the question of "why" for the strategy selection, explains procedure, and/or evaluates reasonableness of solution. **Terminology** Uses appropriate terminology and notation.	**Justification** Fully answers the question of "why" for the strategy selection, explains procedure, and/or evaluates reasonableness of solution. **Terminology** Uses some appropriate terminology or notation.	**Justification** Incompletely answers the question of "why" for the strategy selection; explains procedure; and/or evaluates reasonableness of solution. **Terminology** Uses some appropriate terminology or notation.	**Justification** Provides very little or no explanation of what was done and why. **Terminology** Uses limited or inappropriate terminology or notation.

(Used with permission: Region 4 Education Service Center)

region 4 Educated Solutions

TASK 4.3 *Use the rubric on the previous page to evaluate the work in each of the student case studies.*

Phong

a. Yes No Student arrives at a correct solution?				
	4	3	2	1
b. Conceptual Knowledge				
c. Procedural Knowledge				
d. Communication				

Belkiz

a. Yes No Student arrives at a correct solution?				
	4	3	2	1
b. Conceptual Knowledge				
c. Procedural Knowledge				
d. Communication				

Randy

a. Yes No Student arrives at a correct solution?				
	4	3	2	1
b. Conceptual Knowledge				
c. Procedural Knowledge				
d. Communication				

Rocio

a. Yes No Student arrives at a correct solution?				
	4	3	2	1
b. Conceptual Knowledge				
c. Procedural Knowledge				
d. Communication				

Favian

a. Yes No Student arrives at a correct solution?				
	4	3	2	1
b. Conceptual Knowledge				
c. Procedural Knowledge				
d. Communication				

The data gathered from a rubric used to score a performance assessment early in the year can serve as a baseline to evaluate learning as the year progresses. It is important to remember that the student should be allowed to communicate in ways appropriate to his proficiency level. Performance assessments should be gradually implemented, first with teacher "think-alouds," then by groups producing together, and only then should students work on a performance assessment individually.

Cognitive Supports

Big Ideas

- English language learners come from backgrounds in which the curriculum may emphasize skills and concepts not emphasized in U.S. schools or vice versa.

- Students may represent numbers and numerical relationships differently.

  - Use both verbal and non-verbal clues to determine whether misconceptions are language-based or concept-based.

  - Use a variety of tools, strategies, and activities to encourage students' understanding, participation in, and communication of mathematical concepts.

    - Using authentic assessments will yield a valuable view of student learning and progress.

Points to Ponder

How do we tie together supporting English language learners' affective, language, and cognitive needs?

What does this look like in the classroom?

region 4
Educated Solutions

Chapter 5: *A 5E Lesson*

Learning without thought is labor lost; thought without learning is perilous.
- Confucius

Components of an Effective Lesson

*I*n the first four chapters, we examined needs of English language learners and how to support them in the affective, linguistic, and cognitive domains. The question now arises as to how to incorporate the tools, practices, and strategies into practical classroom use. Perhaps you are asking yourself:

- What does a lesson look like that meets the needs of my English language learners?

- How can I meet the needs of my English language learners and still meet the needs of other students in my classroom?

Echevarria, Vogt, and Short (2004) identify critical instructional features necessary for the academic and language development of English language learners. They are:

Lesson Preparation
Planning should result in lessons that enable students to make connections between their knowledge and experiences and the new information being taught.

Building Background
A student's background impacts his or her ability to recall and elaborate on a topic better than those with limited knowledge of the topic. When students lack background on a topic, the teacher intervenes to build vocabulary, connect the topic to the background the students already have, and assist students in building their own backgrounds through engaging activities and graphic organizers.

Comprehensible Input
Comprehensible input involves speaking slowly, using gestures, drawing and showing pictures, providing hands-on activities, and actively building vocabulary and concept development.

Strategies
Teaching students to be aware of their own thinking, helping them to organize the information they are expected to learn, and encouraging them to engage in group discussion or cooperative learning to solve problems accelerates the learning process.

region *4*
Educated Solutions

A 5E Lesson

Interaction

In many classrooms, there is excessive teacher talk. Instead of teachers talking and students listening or taking notes, students should be interacting as they collaborativly investigate solving problems.

Practice/Application

Students more rapidly progress in mastering content objectives when routinely provided with opportunities to engage in hands-on activities and to use manipulatives, just as it is much more effective to learn to ride a bicycle by doing instead of watching someone else ride it.

Lesson Delivery

The most effective teachers minimize non-productive time. These teachers come well-prepared, possess good classroom management skills, and spend little time making announcements and returning papers. They maximize engaged time in which students actively participate in the instructional process.

Assessment

Effective teachers realize it is important to evaluate student learning throughout the lesson and, particularly at the end of the lesson, to determine how well they have understood the concepts and vocabulary. Determining who is ready to move on and who needs additional instruction is at the heart of effective assessment and instruction and is essential to student success.

So how do I incorporate these critical instructional features into my real-life classroom? What is a research-based instructional model that can help me structure my lesson?

An effective lesson which provides the most impact on student achievement ensures that students are actively engaged in learning as well as reflecting upon their learning to make sense of their activities and provides opportunities to use, extend, and apply what is learned. **The Five E Instructional Model** developed/modified by Roger W. Bybee, past executive director of the National Research Council and Center for Science, Mathematics, and Engineering Education, provides such a model. Learning something new or understanding something familiar in greater depth involves making sense of both our prior experiences and first-hand knowledge gained from new explorations. He components of the Five E Instructional Model (Trowbridge and Bybee, 1996) are:

(1) **ENGAGE:** The instructor initiates this stage by asking well-chosen questions, defining a problem to be solved, or by showing something intriguing. The activity should be designed to interest students in the problem and to make connections to past and present learning.

(2) **EXPLORE:** The exploration stage provides the opportunity for students to become directly involved with the key concepts of the lesson through guided exploration that requires them to probe, inquire, and question. As we learn, the puzzle pieces (ideas and concepts necessary to solve the problem) begin to fit together or have to be broken down and reconstructed several times. In this stage, instructors observe and listen to students as they interact with each other and the activity. Instructors provide probing questions to help students clarify their understanding of major concepts and redirect the questions when necessary.

(3) **EXPLAIN:** In the explanation stage, collaborative learning teams begin to sequence logically events/facts from the investigation and communicate these findings to each other and the instructor. The instructor, acting in a facilitation role, uses this phase to offer further explanations and provide additional meaning or information, such as correct terminology. Giving labels or correct terminology is far more

meaningful and helpful in retention if it is done after the learner has had a direct experience. The explanation stage is used to record the learner's development and grasp of the key ideas and concepts of the lesson.

(4) **ELABORATE:** The elaboration stage allows for students to extend and expand what they have learned in the first three stages and connect this knowledge with their prior learning to create understanding. It is critical that instructors verify students understanding during this stage.

(5) **EVALUATE:** Throughout the learning experiences, the ongoing process of evaluation allows the instructor to determine whether the learner has reached the desired level of understanding the key ideas and concepts. More formal evaluation can be conducted at this stage.

The following table summarizes how the 5E Instructional Model provides the components of an effective lesson.

5E Phase	Lesson Preparation	Building Background	Comprehensible Input	Strategies	Interaction	Practical Application	Lesson Delivery	Assessment
Engage	✓	✓	✓	✓	✓		✓	
Explore	✓		✓	✓	✓	✓	✓	
Explain	✓		✓	✓	✓	✓	✓	
Elaborate	✓		✓	✓	✓	✓	✓	
Evaluate	✓			✓	✓	✓		✓

If monitoring the student's progress indicates he/she has not mastered the learning, the instructor should reenter the student at the appropriate point in the instructional model. Connections between past and present learning may need to be reiterated as they relate to the activity used in the engagement phase. Different materials may need to be used to reinforce concepts, processes, and skills investigated during the exploration phase. The instructor may need to provide additional examples to provide extended time during the explanation phase to facilitate the students' understanding of the key ideas and concepts. Guided-practice activities may need further teacher support to connect, extend, and transfer learning to new situations; increased feedback may need to be provided.

Making Math Accessible for English Language Learners examines two mathematics lessons. In the remainder of this chapter, we will examine a 5E lesson entitled "Investigating Quadratic Relationships" and how it meets the needs of English language learners. In Chapter 6, we will examine a traditional textbook lesson and how to adapt it for English language learners.

A 5E Lesson

Chapter 5: *A 5E Lesson*

Investigating Quadratic Relationships

	TEKS addressed in this lesson:
A.1(A)	Describe independent and dependent quantities in functional relationships.
A.1(B)	Gather and record data and use data sets to determine functional relationships between quantities;
A.1(C)	Describe functional relationships for given problem situations and write equations or inequalities to answer questions arising from the situations.
A.1(D)	Represent relationships among quantities using concrete models, tables, graphs, diagrams, verbal descriptions, equations, and inequalities.
A.1(E)	Interpret and make decisions, predictions, and critical judgements from functional relationships.
A.2(A)	Identify and sketch the general forms of linear ($y = x$) and **quadratic ($y = x^2$)** parent functions.
A.2(D)	Collect and organize data, make and interpret scatter plots (including recognizing positive, negative, or no correlation for data approximating linear situations), and model, predict, and make decisions and critical judgements in problem situations.
A.3(B)	Look for patterns and represent generalizations algebraically.
A.9(A)	Determine the domain and range for quadratic functions in given situations.
A.9(D)	Analyze graphs of quadratic functions and draw conclusions.
A.10(A)	Solve quadratic equations using concrete models, tables, graphs, and algebraic methods.
A.10(B)	Make connections among the solutions (roots) of quadratic equations, the zeros of their related functions, and the horizontal intercepts (*x*-intercepts) of the graph of the function.

Materials

Advanced preparation:

- Copies of student activity sheets

For each student:

- Graphing calculator
- **Toothpick Squares** activity sheet
- **How Many Squares** activity sheet
- **How Many Toothpicks** activity sheet
- **Square-to-Square** activity sheet

For each student group of 3 - 4 students:

- About 200 toothpicks
- Chart paper *(optional)*
- Meter sticks *(optional)*
- Markers *(optional)*

Engage

The **Engage** portion of the lesson is designed to interest students in patterns that can be generated using toothpicks.

1. Distribute the Toothpick Squares activity sheet. Students should use toothpicks to solve puzzle 1 and puzzle 2.

   Note: The blank student pages are in the Appendix and can be copied only for the students of a teacher with a purchased copy of this book.

2. After each student has had time to work on the puzzles, ask the student groups to share their solutions with the whole class.

   Note: The puzzle 2 has two possible solutions.

3. Prompt students to work in their groups to answer questions 1 through 4.

4. Debrief the activity using the Facilitation Questions.

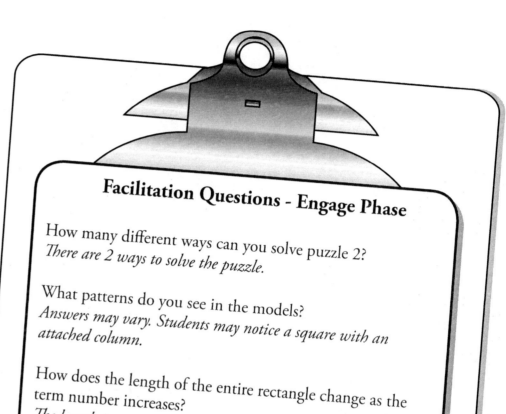

Facilitation Questions - Engage Phase

How many different ways can you solve puzzle 2?
There are 2 ways to solve the puzzle.

What patterns do you see in the models?
Answers may vary. Students may notice a square with an attached column.

How does the length of the entire rectangle change as the term number increases?
The length increases by 1 each time the term number increases.

How does the width of the entire rectangle change as the term number increases?
The width increases by 1 each time the term number increases.

How are the length and the width of each term related to each other?
The length is always one more than the width.

A 5E Lesson

Toothpicks Squares

Often toothpicks are used to create puzzles. Use toothpicks to build the puzzles below, then try to find the solution.

Puzzle 1: Remove 3 toothpicks so there are 3 squares remaining. Sketch your solution.

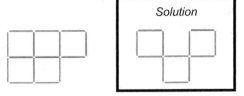

Solution

Puzzle 2: Remove 8 toothpicks so there are 4 squares remaining. Sketch your solution.

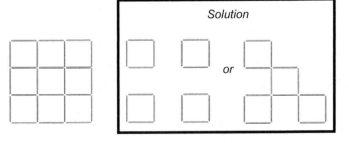

Solution

or

1. Toothpicks can also be used to build models of terms in a sequence. What patterns do you notice in the sequence below?

Term 1

Term 2

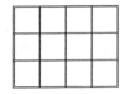

Term 3

2. **Use toothpicks to build the first three terms shown in the sequence in question number 1. Then build and sketch the models for terms 4 and 5.**

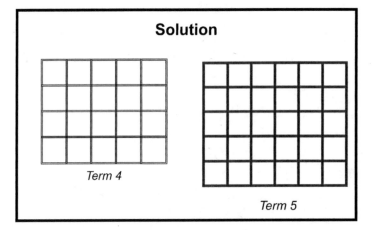

Solution

Term 4

Term 5

3. **Explain how you determined the models for terms 4 and 5.**

   Answers may vary. Students may have noticed the pattern in the length and width of the rectangles.

4. **How could you determine the number of squares in the model for any term number?**

   Answers may vary. Students should realize by developing a function rule they can determine the number of squares for any term number.

	Debriefing a 5E Lesson		
Phase of the 5E Instructional Model	**Understanding**	**Participating/Processing**	**Communicating**
Engage	How does this phase stimulate curiosity? *Students are given 2 tactile puzzles to solve.* How does this phase activate prior knowledge? *Patterns are used to remind students of concept of area.*	What questions could be raised by students? *What do I already know about this? Why is the pattern happening?* What accommodations are included in this phase? *Pictures (graphics) Realia (toothpicks) Use of multiple senses* How is learning made more accessible? *Cooperative learning*	Student - Student *Groups of 3-4. The focus in this phase is on student interaction.* Student - Teacher *Student may ask for clarification but should be allowed to work without teacher intervention.* Teacher - Student *Teacher is a facilitator in this phase.*

A 5E Lesson

Hot Tip!

The Engage phase is used to create interest and make connections to prior knowledge.

Hot Tip!

Suspend judgement while asking probing questions to find out what the student already knows.

Explore

The **Explore** portion of the lesson provides the student with an opportunity to be actively involved in the exploration of the mathematical concepts addressed. This part of the lesson is designed for groups of three to four students.

1. Distribute the **How Many Squares** activity sheet.

2. Have students follow the directions on the activity sheet to organize the data and explore the relationship between the term number and the number of squares.

All children can learn and succeed but not the same day in the same way.

- James Spady

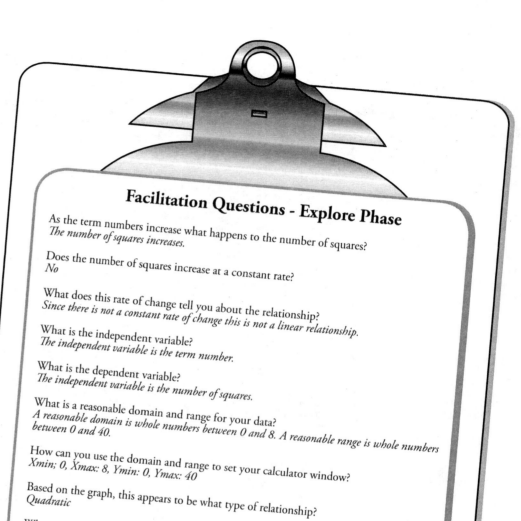

Facilitation Questions - Explore Phase

As the term numbers increase what happens to the number of squares?
The number of squares increases.

Does the number of squares increase at a constant rate?
No

What does this rate of change tell you about the relationship?
Since there is not a constant rate of change this is not a linear relationship.

What is the independent variable?
The independent variable is the term number.

What is the dependent variable?
The independent variable is the number of squares.

What is a reasonable domain and range for your data?
A reasonable domain is whole numbers between 0 and 8. A reasonable range is whole numbers between 0 and 40.

How can you use the domain and range to set your calculator window?
Xmin: 0, Xmax: 8, Ymin: 0, Ymax: 40

Based on the graph, this appears to be what type of relationship?
Quadratic

What is the parent function for this type of relationship?
$y = x^2$

How can you find the areas of each rectangle?
Multiply the length by the width.

How can you use the square part of each rectangle, 1 by 1, 2 by 2, 3 by 3, etc. to determine the function rule?
The number of squares is always the area of the square plus the term number.

How Many Squares?

To determine the number of squares in the model for any term number, you will use the data to determine a function rule to model your data. Then use your function rule to find the number of squares in any term.

1. **Use your models from the Toothpick Squares activity to complete the table below.**

   Toothpick Squares

Term Number	Number of Squares
1	2
2	6
3	12
4	20
5	30

2. **What patterns do you observe in your table?**

   Answer may vary. Students should realize the number of squares increases but not at a constant rate.

3. **Generate a scatter plot of your data. Identify your viewing window and sketch your graph.**

   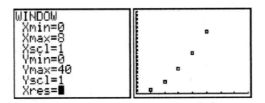

4. **What observations can you make about your graph?**

   Answer may vary. Students should realize the graph does not appear to be linear.

5. **Use the process column to develop an appropriate function rule to model your data.**

   Sample process (see Explain phase for additional examples)

Term Number	Process	Number of Squares
1	$1 \cdot 1 + 1$ or $1^2 + 1$	2
2	$2 \cdot 2 + 2$ or $2^2 + 2$	6
3	$3 \cdot 3 + 3$ or $3^2 + 3$	12
4	$4 \cdot 4 + 4$ or $4^2 + 4$	20
5	$5 \cdot 5 + 5$ or $5^2 + 5$	30
n	$n \cdot n + n$ or $n^2 + n$	

6. **Test the rule over your scatter plot. Write your function rule and sketch your graph.**

   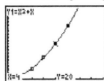

7. **If this pattern continues, what will be the number of squares in the 15th term? Justify your answer.**

   240 squares (see Explain phase for detailed solutions)

8. **If there are 650 squares in the model, what is the term number? Justify your answer.**

   25th term (See Explain phase for detailed solutions.)

© 2006 Region 4 Education Service Center.

A 5E Lesson

Debriefing a 5E Lesson			
Phase of the 5E Instructional Model	**Understanding**	**Participating/Processing**	**Communicating**
Explore	What concepts are explored? *Area (number of squares) increases but not at a constant (linear) rate.* What vocabulary is needed for this phase? Prior vocabulary: *Independent* *Dependent* *Domain* *Range* *Term number* *Function rule* New vocabulary *Quadratic relationship* *Quadratic parent function y = x²*	What accommodations are included in this phase? *Table* *Graphing calculator* *Scaffolding questions* How is learning made more accessible? *Cooperative learning. Assign peer tutors if needed.*	Student - Student *Groups of 3-4. The focus in this phase is on student interaction.* Student - Teacher *Students may ask for clarification but should be allowed to explore with the group.* Teacher - Student *Teacher is a facilitator in this phase.*

Hot Tip! In the Explore phase students work together with the teacher asking facilitating questions.

Hot Tip! Allow time for students to problem solve through tasks.

Hot Tip! Listen to what students are saying as they interact.

Explain

The **Explain** portion of the lesson is directed by the teacher to allow the students to formalize their understanding of the TEKS addressed in the lesson. In this phase, debrief the **How Many Squares** activity sheet from the Explore Phase. Use the Facilitation Questions to prompt student groups to share their responses to the data analysis.

- Debrief the **How Many Squares** activity sheet.

- Ask students to share how they developed their scatter plots and why they chose this method. If students had difficulty developing the scatter plot, be sure to explain the procedure in detail.

Sample answer using a graphing calculator:

Enter data into the STAT lists.

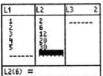

Set up the STAT PLOT, choose an appropriate window, and view the graph.

 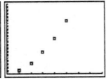

- Ask students to share how they developed their function rule and why they chose this method. If students had difficulty developing the function rule be sure to explain the procedure in detail. Also explain the different methods for determining the function rule. Students will need this information to be successful in the Elaborate phase of this lesson.

Hot Tip!

In the Explain phase help students formalize what they have explored. Be sure to correct any misconceptions.

Hot Tip!

Encourage students to question each others' results.

A 5E Lesson

In this example point out the area of the square in each model then relate it to the process column.

Sample answers using models and number patterns to complete the process column.

Term Number	Diagram	Process	Number Squares
1		$1 \cdot 2$ *or* $1(1 + 1)$	2
2		$2 \cdot 3$ *or* $2(2 + 1)$	6
3		$3 \cdot 4$ *or* $3(3 + 1)$	12
4		$4 \cdot 5$ *or* $4(4 + 1)$	20
5		$5 \cdot 6$ *or* $5(5 + 1)$	30
n		$n(n + 1)$ *or* $n^2 + n$	

A 5E Lesson

A 5E Lesson

Sample answers using Finite Differences to determine the rule:

Since second differences are constant we know this is a quadratic relationship. One half of the second difference is, a, in $ax^2 + bx + c$. This gives us $1x^2 + bx + c$. The first difference, which we found by working backwards, is $a + b$ in $ax^2 + bx + c$. So $2 = 1 + b$, which gives $b = 1$. We now have $1x^2 + 1x + c$. In our table, when $x = 0$, $f(x) = 0$ so c must equal 0.

This gives us the rule **$1x^2 + 1x + 0$ or $x^2 + x$** .

Term Number	Number of Squares
0	0
1	2
2	6
3	12
4	20
5	30

First Differences: 2, 4, 6, 8, 10

Second Differences: 2, 2, 2, 2

- Ask students to share how they predicted the number of squares in the 15th term and why they chose that method.

Students may have solved using the graph or the table feature of their graphing calculator.

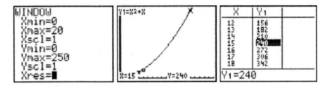

Students may have solved the problem symbolically using the home screen on their calculator.

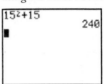

- Ask students to share how they found the term number when the number of squares was 650.

Students may have solved using the graph or the table feature of their graphing calculator.

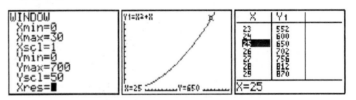

Students may have set up an equation solved the problem symbolically.

$$n^2 + n = 650$$
$$n^2 + n - 650 = 0$$
$$(n + 26)(n - 25) = 0$$
$$(n + 26) = 0 \text{ or } (n - 25) = 0$$
$$n = -26 \text{ or } n = 25$$

Students may have solved the problem by finding the intersection of $y = x^2 + x$ *and* $y = 650$.

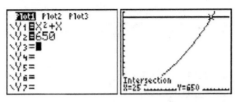

Students may have solved the problem by finding the zeros of $y = x^2 + x - 650$.

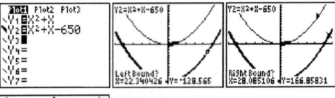

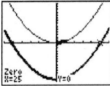

Hot Tip!

Have a student operate the overhead graphing calculator or emulator while you monitor and question.

We will now formalize the vocabulary and concepts for quadratic functions. Distribute blank vocabulary organizers and facilitate as student groups complete their organizers.

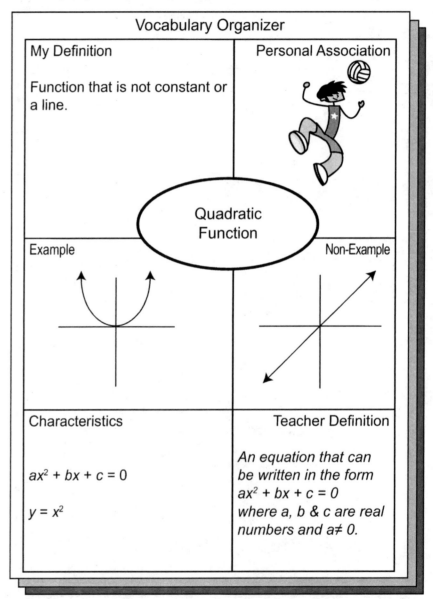

Vocabulary Organizer

My Definition

Function that is not constant or a line.

Personal Association

Quadratic Function

Example

Non-Example

Characteristics

$ax^2 + bx + c = 0$

$y = x^2$

Teacher Definition

An equation that can be written in the form $ax^2 + bx + c = 0$ *where a, b & c are real numbers and a ≠ 0.*

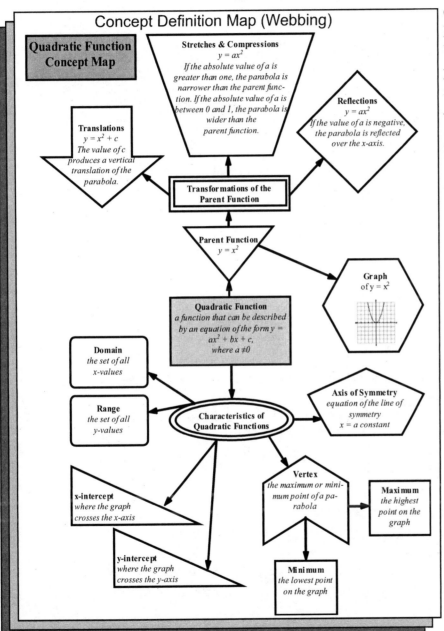

Concept Definition Map (Webbing)

Used with permission, *Accelerated Curriculum, Exit Level*, Region 4 ESC.

Concepts can be organized using concept definition maps, also known as webbings. You may want to make a transparency of the blank concept definition map to fill in, or you might prefer to draw your own as students are filling in their copies. Have the students fill in the definition of quadratic function in the middle rectangle. Ask what the parent function is and what the graph looks like. Fill in those boxes. Ask students what the characteristics of quadratic functions are. Fill in the appropriate areas with definitions as they answer. Then, ask the students to describe the different transformations to quadratic functions they discovered in the Explore phase. Write their answers in the appropriate places.

A 5E Lesson

Hot Tip!

Instead of completing the entire concept definition map when the concept is introduced, complete it during the course of the unit as vocabulary and concepts are encountered.

A 5E Lesson

	Debriefing a 5E Lesson		
Phase of the 5E Instructional Model	**Understanding**	**Participating/Processing**	**Communicating**
Explain	What connections are essential for the student to understand? *Quadratic relations do not have a constant rate of change. If the second differences are constant, the relationship is quadratic.* What new vocabulary is introduced? *Quadratic relationship* *Second differences* *Roots* *Zeros*	What algorithms are connected to the concept? *Solving quadratic equations* *Factoring (one way to solve).* What scaffolding questions guide students to an understanding of the concept? *What patterns do you observe in your table?* *Generate a scatter plot.* *Identify your viewing window and sketch your graph.* *What observations can you make about your graph?* *Use the process column to develop an appropriate function rule to model your data.* *Test the rule over your scatter plot. Write your function rules and sketch your graph.* Instead of just asking the last 2 questions, *guide students* through a series of easier questions that will help them in answering the last 2 questions: *If this pattern continues, what will be the number of square in the 15th term?* *If there are 650 squares, what is the term number?* What accommodations are included in this phase? How is learning made more accessible? *Vocabulary concept map* *Can use table, graph, or graphing calculator to explain.* *Flexible grouping. Assign peer tutors if needed.*	Student - Student *Explain possible answers to each other.* Student - Teacher *The student shows how he solved the problem, perhaps by showing the table, graph, or calculator screen.* Teacher - Student *Teacher debriefs activity using facilitating questions.* *Encourage students to examine alternative methods of solving problems.*

Hot Tip!

Phase in the use of vocabulary organizers and concept definition maps.

Elaborate

The **Elaborate** portion of the lesson provides an opportunity for the student to apply the concepts of the TEKS within a new situation. In this lesson, students will generate a more complex quadratic function. This part of the lesson is designed for groups of three to four students.

1. Distribute the **How Many Toothpicks** activity sheet. Students should follow the directions to solve the problem.

2. Use the Facilitation Questions to redirect students as necessary.

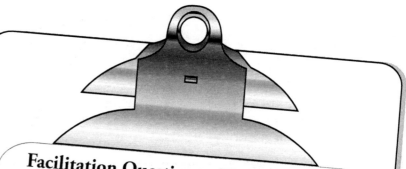

Facilitation Questions - Elaborate Phase

As the term numbers increase what happens to the number of toothpicks? *The number of toothpicks increases.*

Does the number of toothpicks increase at a constant rate? *No.*

What does this rate of change tell you about the relationship? *Since there is not a constant rate of change this is not a linear relationship.*

What is the independent variable? *The independent variable is the term number.*

What is the dependent variable? *The dependent variable is the number of toothpicks.*

What is a reasonable domain and range for your data? *A reasonable domain is whole numbers between 0 and 7. A reasonable range is whole numbers between 0 and 80.*

How can you use the domain and range to set your calculator window? *Xmin: 0, Xmax: 7, Ymin: 0, Ymax: 80*

Based on the graph, this appears to be what type of relationship? *Quadratic*

What is the parent function for this type of relationship? $y = x^2$

What is the constant second difference in your table values? *4*

What must be the value of a in $ax^2 + bx + c$? *Since a is one-half for the constant second different, a = 2.*

What is the first difference? *By working backward to 9, we find the first difference to be 6.*

Since the first difference equals a + b, what is the value of b? *4*

What must be the value of c? *c = 1 since the number of toothpicks is 1 when the term number is 0.*

Hot Tip!

Store calculators in a hanging shoe bag for easy access and as an easy way to notice if any calculators are missing.

A 5E Lesson

How Many Toothpicks?

1. **Use your models from the Toothpick Squares activity to determine the number of toothpicks necessary to build each model then complete the table below.**

Term Number	Number of Toothpicks
1	7
2	17
3	31
4	49
5	71

2. **What patterns do you observe in your table?**

   Answers may vary. Students should realize the number of squares increases but not at a constant rate.

3. **Generate a scatter plot of your data. Identify your window and sketch your graph.**

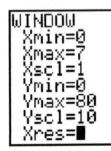 

4. **What observations can you make about your graph?**

   Answer may vary. Students should realize the graph does not appear to be linear.

5. **Use the process column to develop an appropriate function rule to model your data.**

   Sample process (See Explain phase for additional examples)

Term Number	Process	Number of Toothpicks
1	$2 \cdot n^2 + 4 \cdot 1 + 1$	7
2	$2 \cdot n^2 + 4 \cdot 2 + 1$	17
3	$2 \cdot n^2 + 4 \cdot 3 + 1$	31
4	$2 \cdot n^2 + 4 \cdot 4 + 1$	49
5	$2 \cdot n^2 + 4 \cdot 5 + 1$	71
n	$2 \cdot n^2 + 4 \cdot n + 1$	

6. **Test the rule over your scatter plot. Write your function rule and sketch your graph.**
   Sample function rule: $y = 2n^2 + 4n + 1$

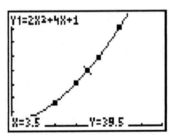

region 4
Educated Solutions

7. If this pattern continues, what will be the number of toothpicks in the 15th term? Justify your answer.

511 toothpicks. Solve with a graph and table.

 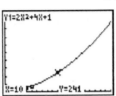 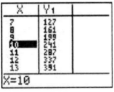

8. If it takes 241 toothpicks to build the model, what is the term number? Justify your answer.

10th term

Solve with a graph and table:

 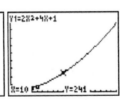

Solve symbolically:

$$2n^2 + 4n + 1 = 241$$
$$2n^2 + 4n - 240 = 0$$
$$(2n + 24)(n - 10) = 0$$
$$(2n + 24) = 0 \text{ or } (n - 10) = 0$$
$$n = -12 \text{ or } n = 10$$

Solve by finding the intersection of $y = 2x^2 + 4x + 1$ and $y = 241$.

 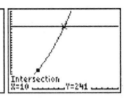

Solve by finding the zeros of $y = 2x^2 + 4x - 240$.

 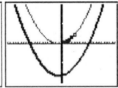

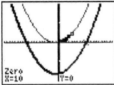

A 5E Lesson

Debriefing a 5E Lesson			
Phase of the 5E Instructional Model	**Understanding**	**Participating/Processing**	**Communicating**
	How is the new concept applied or extended?	How (if at all) must the algorithms be applied?	Student - Student
	This time the student is finding the number of toothpicks needed to develop the pattern. Again, this phase is tied back to the Engage Phase with the original models.	*Factoring can be used to solve quadratic equations, although they could be solved in other ways.*	*Flexible grouping.*
			Student - Teacher
	How is the use of vocabulary encouraged?	What accommodations are included in this phase? How is learning made more accessible?	*Opportunities not only for verbal and written communication but with tables, graphs, and the graphing calculator.*
	It is revisited in the extension of the concept.	*Use of tables, graphs, and graphing calculator.*	Teacher - Student
			Facilitating questions.
	What understanding must the student have to be successful with this phase of the lesson?	*Flexible grouping. Assign peer tutors if needed.*	
Elaborate	*Quadratic relationships.*		

Hot Tip!
In the Elaborate phase, encourage students to use formal labels and definitions that were developed earlier in the lesson.

Hot Tip!
Provide opportunities for students to discover the benefit of sharing explanations with each other.

Evaluate

Throughout the lesson, the teacher determines whether the learning has reached the desired level of understanding of the key concepts. A more formal assessment is appropriate in the Evaluate phase of the 5E Model.

You will recall that performance assessments, such as "Square-to-Square," are intended to allow students to arrive at the solution in a variety of different ways. Some students may solve using a table, while others may use the graphing calculator, and still others may solve algebraically.

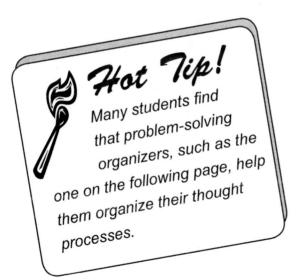

Hot Tip!

Many students find that problem-solving organizers, such as the one on the following page, help them organize their thought processes.

Square-to-Square

Orlando has the popular game, Square-to-Square, on his cell phone. Each time he successfully completes a game a new more difficult game board appears. The game boards for levels 1, 2, and 3 are show below.

Level 1

Level 2

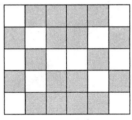
Level 3

If Orlando gets to level 10 how many shaded squares will his game board contain? Justify your answer.

Answer: 270

(See a possible student response on the following page.)

A 5E Lesson

See

What do we know?
The patterns in levels 1, 2 and 3.

What do we need to know?
How many squares are in level 10.

Plan

Compare the stages to find the pattern.

What will be our first step?
Find the length and width in terms of y.

What will be our second step?
Multiply the length and width.

What will be our third step?
Find the number of white squares.
Subtract the white squares to get the shaded ones.

Problem:

Do

Step 1:
$[(2x - 1) (2x)] - (x^2 + x)$
total area - white squares

Step 2:
$(4x^2 - 2x) - (x^2 + x)$

Step 3:
$3x^2 - 3x$

Reflect

We know our solution is reasonable because. . .
We tried equation with Stages 1-4 and then 10. It worked with all of them. We used the table in the calculator and saw that it worked for any stage.

These things helped us find a solution:
We drew the fourth stage, and that helped us find the pattern for the white squares. We checked by entering the data in the stat plot and finding the quadratic regression line. It didn't match our original equation, but it did after we simplified our equation.

Hot Tip!

Use these verbs to guide you in creating appropriate assessments:

Beginning	Choose Draw Point Select	Group Label List Name
Intermediate	The above + Answer Describe Define Compare Contrast Explain	
Advanced	The above + Analyze Evaluate Justify	
Advanced High	Any of the above	

How does the 5E lesson meet the needs of English language learners?

Meeting the Needs of ELLs		
Affective	**Linguistic**	**Cognitive**
• Flexible grouping *Peer tutors if needed.* • Students can help each other. • Concrete objects are used to enhance learning, make the concept easier to understand, and lower student stress. • Teacher is the facilitator not "the sage on the stage."	• Student lesson is in sans-serif font. • Use of visuals, graphics, and simplified language makes the concept more accessible. • Use of charts and tables provides more non-verbal learning opportunities. • Use of calculators enhances understanding in a non-verbal way. • Student-student, student-teacher and teacher-student dialog provide opportunities for language enrichment. • Students can respond in non-verbal and reduced-verbal ways.	• The Engage portion activates prior knowledge . • The puzzles stimulate interest. • Comparing and contrasting stimulates long-term memory. • Group work allows students to learn from each other. • Use of tools (graphing calculator) makes learning the concept more efficient. • Assessment measures mathematical proficiency, not reading proficiency. • Use of scaffolding questions builds understanding. • Opportunities for the student to think about his/her own thinking increases metacognitive skills.

Hot Tip!
It is important to maintain a nuturing environment, establish support, and value each student on a continuing basis.

Hot Tip!
Frequently ask students to respond on personal response boards or chart paper.

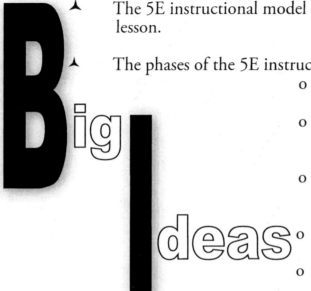

▲ The 5E instructional model provides a practical vehicle for implementing the components of an effective lesson.

▲ The phases of the 5E instructional model are:

o **Engage**: Designed to interest students in the problem and to make connections between past and present learning.

o **Explore**: Designed to provide the opportunity for students to become directly involved with the key concepts with the teacher observing and listening to students as they interact with each other.

o **Explain**: Designed for the teacher to act as a facilitator to formalize terminology, correct any misconceptions, and provide further meaning or information.

o **Elaborate**: Designed to allow students to extend and expand what they have learned in the first 3 phases.

o **Evaluate**: Designed to allow the teacher to determine whether the learner has reached the desired level of understanding the key ideas and concepts.

*H*ow might I begin to implement 5E lessons in my classroom?

*W*hen might be a "comfortable" place in my currriculum to try a 5E lesson?

*H*ow might I adapt traditional lessons to incorporate some of the benefits to students the 5E instructional model provides?

Notes

A 5E Lesson

region4
Educated Solutions

Chapter 6: *Adapting a Traditional Textbook Lesson*

A small part of even the most reluctant student wants to learn.
- Anonymous

A Traditional Textbook Lesson

*T*raditional textbook lessons present several concerns. The lesson format generally lends itself to teacher-centered instruction instead of student-centered instruction. The content of standard textbook lessons rarely includes examples and problems with the cognitive rigor necessary to prepare students for success, whether success is measured by standardized tests or readiness for post-high-school education. Such lessons rarely include strategies for building common background, developing vocabulary, providing comprehensibility, and solving authentic problems in an atmosphere ripe for interaction. Therefore, teachers are often faced with the challenge of adapting traditional lessons to meet the needs of English language learners.

The following section represents what a teacher might see in a traditional Geometry textbook lesson in which students explore slopes of lines, including parallel and perpendicular lines, prior to exploring properties of parallel and perpendicular lines and properties of polygons.

Tell me and I'll forget, show me and I may remember, involve me and I'll understand.
- Chinese Proverb

Chapter 3-1

Slope of Parallel and Perpendicular Lines

WHAT YOU WILL LEARN

To find the slopes of lines including parallel and perpendicular lines

WHY IT IS IMPORTANT TO LEARN

Parallel and perpendicular lines appear frequently in geometric figures and are represented in art, architecture, and engineering.

VOCABULARY TO REMEMBER

- Slope
- Parallel
- Perpendicular

The slope of a line is the ratio of the vertical rise of the line to the horizontal run of the line.

$$\text{slope} = \frac{\text{rise}}{\text{run}}$$

The slope m of a line containing points (x_1, y_1) and (x_2, y_2) is defined as

$$m = \frac{y_2 - y_1}{x_2 - x_1} .$$

Example 1   Find the slope of the line.

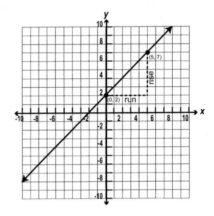

Let $(0, 2)$ be (x_1, y_1) and $(5, 7)$ be (x_2, y_2) .

Substitute the values into the formula.

$$m = \frac{y_2 - y_1}{x_2 - x_1}$$

$$m = \frac{7 - 2}{5 - 0}$$

$$m = \frac{5}{5} = 1$$

Notice that when the value of m is positive, the slope of the line rises to the right.

Example 2   Find the slope of the line.

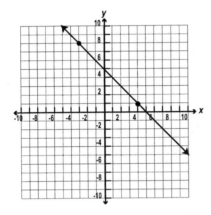

Let $(-3, 8)$ be (x_1, y_1) and $(4, 1)$ be (x_2, y_2) .

Substitute the values into the formula.

$$m = \frac{y_2 - y_1}{x_2 - x_1}$$

$$m = \frac{1 - 8}{4 - -3}$$

$$m = \frac{-7}{7} = -1$$

Notice that when the value of m is negative, the slope of the line falls to the right.

Example 3   Find the slope of the line.

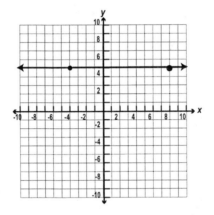

Let $(-4, 5)$ be (x_1, y_1) and $(8, 5)$ be (x_2, y_2) .

Substitute the values into the formula.

$$m = \frac{y_2 - y_1}{x_2 - x_1}$$

$$m = \frac{5 - 5}{8 - -4}$$

$$m = \frac{0}{12} = 0$$

Notice that when the value of m is 0, the line is horizontal.

Adapting a
Textbook Lesson

Example 4 Find the slope of the line.

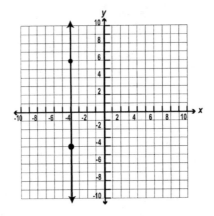

Let $(-4, 6)$ be (x_1, y_1) and $(-4, -4)$ be (x_2, y_2).

Substitute the values into the formula.

$$m = \frac{y_2 - y_1}{x_2 - x_1}$$

$$m = \frac{-4 - 6}{-4 - {}^{-}4}$$

$$m = \frac{-10}{0} \text{ or } \textit{undefined}$$

Notice that when the value of m is undefined, the line is vertical.

Example 5

Given points A (4, -3), B (-3, -1), and Q (1, 2), find the coordinates of a point P such that $\overrightarrow{AB} \parallel \overrightarrow{PQ}$.

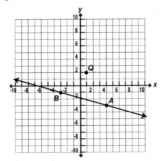

Since we know $\overrightarrow{AB} \parallel \overrightarrow{PQ}$, then the slopes of the two lines must be the same. First, find the slope of $\overrightarrow{AB}$.

The slope of $\overrightarrow{AB}$ = $\frac{-3 - -1}{4 - -3} = \frac{-2}{7}$.

We know the coordinates of Q, but there are infinite possibilities for P. So using (x, y) in the slope formula, we get $\frac{2 - y}{1 - x} = \frac{-2}{7}$.

Split the numerator and denominator to make 2 separate equations and solve.

$1 - x = 7 \qquad 2 - y = -2$

$-x = 6 \qquad -y = -4$

$x = -6 \qquad y = 4$

Thus, one possible set of coordinates for P are (-6, 4).

Example 6

Given points $M(-1, -6)$, $N(3, 2)$, and $R(0, 1)$, find the coordinates of a point S such that $\overrightarrow{RS} \perp \overrightarrow{MN}$.

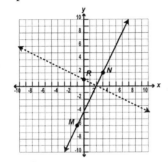

Since we know $\overrightarrow{RS} \perp \overrightarrow{MN}$, then the slopes of the two lines must be opposite reciprocals. First, find the slope of $\overline{MN}$.

The slope of $\overline{MN} = \dfrac{2 - -6}{3 - -1} = \dfrac{8}{4} = \dfrac{2}{1}$. The opposite reciprocal of $\dfrac{2}{1}$ is $-\dfrac{1}{2}$.

We know the coordinates of R, but there are infinite possibilities for S. So using (x, y) and a slope of in the slope formula, we get $\dfrac{1 - y}{0 - x} = -\dfrac{1}{2}$.

Split the numerator and denominator to make 2 separate equations and solve.

$-x = 2 \qquad 1 - y = -1$

$-x = 2 \qquad -y = -2$

$x = -2 \qquad y = 2$

Thus one possible set of coordinates for P is $(-2, 2)$.

Example 7

Graph the points A(-8, -1), B(-3, 4), C(1, 0), and D(-4, -5). Which quadrilateral is represented?

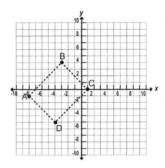

First plot the coordinates and label the points. Find the slope of each side.

The slope of $\overline{AB} = \dfrac{4 - -1}{-3 - -8} = \dfrac{5}{5} = 1$.

The slope of $\overline{BC} = \dfrac{0 - 4}{1 - -3} = \dfrac{-4}{4} = -1$.

The slope of $\overline{CD} = \dfrac{-5 - 0}{-4 - 1} = \dfrac{-5}{-5} = 1$.

The slope of $\overline{DA} = \dfrac{-1 - 5}{-8 - -4} = \dfrac{4}{-4} = -1$.

The opposite sides have the same slopes and, therefore, are parallel to each other. The adjacent sides have slopes that are negative reciprocals, and, therefore, are perpendicular to each other. The figure is a rectangle.

© 2006 Region 4 Education Service Center.

121

Adapting a
Textbook Lesson

Guided Practice

1. What is the slope of the line containing the points (-2, 3) and (2, 1)?

2. Find the slope of the line $y = -3$.

3. Find the slope of the line $x = 4$.

Describe each of the following as parallel, perpendicular, neither parallel nor perpendicular.

4. railroad tracks

5. sides of a *yield* sign

6. adjacent sides of a box

Independent Practice

1. Find the slope of the line graphed below.

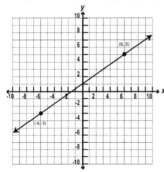

Find the slope, if it exists, of the lines containing these points.

2. (5, -6) (3, -2)

3. $x = 5$

4. $y = -7$

5. $\left(\dfrac{3}{4}, \dfrac{1}{2}\right) \left(\dfrac{1}{4}, -\dfrac{1}{2}\right)$

6. In the figure below, name 3 pairs of parallel lines and 3 pairs of perpendicular lines.

7. Triangle PQR is shown on the coordinate grid below.

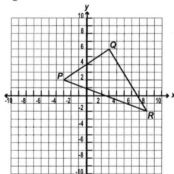

What is the slope of $\overline{PR}$?

Adapting the Traditional Textbook Lesson

We have included a possible adaptation of the preceding traditional textbook lesson for all five phases of the 5E instructional model. However, we encourage you to begin adapting lessons in stages. Study the chart below to help you determine at which stage you would place yourself. If you try to start at Stage 5 and are used to students sitting in rows and using a standard textbook as your curriculum (which may have been a district or building expectation), you will set yourself up for failure by beginning at Stage 5.

Stages of 5E Implementation

Stage 1	Stage 2	Stage 3	Stage 4	Stage 5
I'm really comfortable with directly teaching the material by working at the overhead and having students follow my lead. I use the ancillaries provided with the textbook if I need additional materials.	I occasionally have students work with a partner or small group on an activity or project. I also sometimes have them use tools such as grid paper, patty paper, and graphing calculators, and I look for materials from outside resources to enhance instruction.	I like to have a balance of group and independent work. I am comfortable using a variety of tools and frequently use materials other than the textbook.	I frequently have my students work in groups and am comfortable managing an interactive classroom. I believe it is important for students to work and talk together. I look for activities that are challenging and require students to think a step beyond the lesson objective.	I create many of my own materials and mainly use the textbook as a resource for practice problems. My students routinely work in cooperative groups. I am comfortable with lots of activity in the classroom and enjoy trying innovative things.
Focus on the Engage and Explain phases	**Focus on the Explore phase.**	**Focus on the Evaluate phase.**	**Focus on the Elaborate phase.**	**Put it all together to create a 5E lesson.**

Adapting a Textbook Lesson

Hot Tip!

This self-evaluation is an important step in adapting lessons to the 5E model.

Stage 1

Traditional textbook lessons will not constitute an entire 5E lesson. Decide if the lesson includes an appropriate Engage. If it does not include an activity to stimulate student interest and to activate prior knowledge, think about what tools you have used or would like to use to set the stage for the lesson. If we want students to work with finding slope, possible tools might include the graphing calculator, coordinate grid paper, patty paper or geoboards.

In the Explain phase of the lesson, we want to focus on how to debrief the Explore part of the lesson. You may have used the textbook examples and guided practice problems for exploration. Asking questions that give insight to student processing and providing the opportunity to correct any misconceptions will enhance retention and provide a strong foundation for exploring the concept at greater depth and complexity. Reviewing the facilitation questions in Chapter 5 may be helpful in the continuing journey we all make to strengthen our questioning strategies.

Stage 2

The quality of instruction in the Explore phase of the lesson is one of our most powerful ways to accelerate language and mathematical proficiency. The opportunity is ripe in the Explore phase to link concrete representations to abstract concepts. By carefully evaluating available tools and choosing the most effective ones to encourage student interaction, a forgettable traditional textbook lesson can come to life for students.

The challenge to the teacher is to decide not only which tool would be most effective but to manage a student-centered, interactive classroom. Activities must be well-planned, and expected behaviors must be overtly taught and reinforced throughout the year. Start small, perhaps having students work with a partner for 5 minutes on a specific task. As students become accustomed to expectations and routines, and as you feel more comfortable with student-centered instruction, the size of the groups may be expanded to 3 or 4 students, and the length of time devoted to more complex tasks may be increased.

Stage 3

Appropriately assessing student progress is critical in determining student strengths, weaknesses, and possible misconceptions. Whether using selected response items or performance assessments, assessments should mirror instruction, occur continuously, and provide information about the student's level of understanding. Selected response items, whether multiple choice, true/false, matching, or fill-in-the-blank, can provide information about mastery of the concept as well as areas of deficiency. Performance assessments allow students to demonstrate their understanding by solving a task in one of several possible ways. As discussed earlier, performance assessments should be phased in, and students can benefit from hearing and seeing other students' strategies for solving the same problem.

Stage 4

The Elaborate phase of the lesson allows for an expanded or extended look at the lesson concept. Again, the selection of appropriate tools is important, as is providing affective, linguistic, and cognitive supports so that students are likely to succeed. This phase of the 5E instructional model is often the answer to the question, "How do I get students to think?" Evidence of increased student thinking is not generally instantaneous but compounds with routine implementation of the 5E model.

Stage 5

Frequently seeking out resources that expand student thinking and creating your own materials is an indicator that you know there are more effective means to provide instruction than to directly teach a traditional textbook lesson. The advantage of using the 5E instructional model is that it provides a research-based framework for developing effective materials and deciding the most efficient place in the lesson to include the materials.

Planning

Since we know the 5E instructional model is effective in meeting our students needs, we will use the template on the following pages to organize our thoughts. There is a blank template in Appendix F. When you ask yourself the following questions about previously-developed activities or when you consider new activities, it becomes easier to determine whether an activity or task serves the intended purpose.

- Does the activity interest students in the problem and make connections between past and present learning? (**Engage**)

- Does the activity provide the opportunity for students to become directly involved in the key concepts of the lesson by interacting with each other and the activity? (**Explore**)

- Retention and use of math vocabulary is more meaningful after students have had a direct experience with the concept. Is there an opportunity to formalize the concepts and vocabulary? Is there opportunity for students to draw conclusions and communicate them to each other and the teacher? (**Explain**)

- Does the evaluation allow the teacher to determine whether the learner has reached the desired level of understanding of the key ideas and concepts? (**Evaluate**)

- Does the activity allow students to extend and expand what they learned in the first three stages? (**Elaborate**)

The shell must break before the bird can fly.

- Alfred, Lord Tennyson

5E Lesson Plan

TEKS: G.7B	Content Objective:	Language Objective:	Study/Metacognitive Objective:
Use slopes and equations of lines to investigate geometric relationships including parallel lines, perpendicular lines, and special segments of triangles and other polygons.	The student is expected to find and use slopes of lines, including those of parallel and perpendicular lines. *Note: The focus in this textbook lesson is on finding slopes. The next lesson in the textbook centers on writing equations of lines in polygons graphed on a coordinate plane.*	• Beginning students will demonstrate understanding of key vocabulary using manipulatives and drawings. • Intermediate students will use phrases and short sentences to communicate understanding, both verbally and in writing. • Advanced students will use complete sentences to communicate understanding, both verbally and in writing. • Advanced High students will use complete sentences with descriptive language to communicate understanding.	Students will describe the process they went through to arrive at the answer to the performance assessment; that is, they will justify their solutions, verbally or non-verbally, depending proficiency level.

Hot Tip!

The adaptation of the traditional textbook lesson to the 5E model need not be a daunting task. What is written here expresses what may be in fact a short thought process.

Adapting a Textbook Lesson

Phase of the 5E Instructional Model	Developmental Progression	Activity	Sense-Making	Discourse
Engage	**What tools or materials will I use in this phase to stimulate curiosity?** *Geoboards with rubber bands* **What prior knowledge do I want to activate?** *Triangles and Slopes*	**What activity will I use to stimulate curiosity and activate prior knowledge?** • *Arrange students in groups of 3-4.* • *Instruct students to build a triangle. Ask them to identify the slope of each side.* *(Responses will vary)* • *Use a geoboard to build a right triangle with a hypotenuse having a slope of 1.* *(See Example A on the following page.)*	**What accommodations could be included in this phase?** *Hold up the geoboard and say, "This is a geoboard." "This is a rubberband." Demonstrate how to make a shape on the geoboard.* **How could learning be made more accessible?** *Heterogeneous grouping with attention to including peer support for Beginning and Intermediate ELL.* *Note: Set expectations for using rubber bands and geoboards*	**Student - Student** *Students will work together and discuss their strategies.* **Student - Teacher** *What questions could be raised by students?* *What is a hypotenuse?* **Teacher - Student** *Teacher sets stage for activity, monitors student groups, and checks student work.* **Facilitating Questions** • *Is the triangle you built equilateral, isosceles, or scalene?* • *Is it acute, obtuse or right?* • *What is the rate of change for each side of the triangle?* • *What is the slope of each side?* • *How do you know that?* • *How do you know it is a right triangle?* • *Which lines form the right angle?* • *What is the slope of the hypotenuse?* • *Are the lines that form the sides perpendicular since their slopes have the opposite sign and are reciprocals?* • *Which polygon did you build?* • *Can you build a triangle?* • *Why not?* • *Look at the table on the graphing calculator. Do the points on the graph on the grid paper correspond to those in the table?*
Possible tools to choose from • Graphing calculator • Patty paper • Coordinate grid paper • Geoboards • Realia	**Is there non-conceptual vocabulary that needs to be pre-taught?** *Not in this lesson*	• *Use a geoboard to build a triangle with one side having a slope of 2 and another side having a slope of -2.* *(See Example B on the following page.)* • *Build a figure that has at least one pair of parallel sides.* *(See Example C on the following page.)*		

Hot Tip!

Again... *The adaptation of the traditional textbook lesson to the 5E model need not be a daunting task. What is written here expresses what may be in fact a short thought process.*

Adapting a Textbook Lesson

Example A

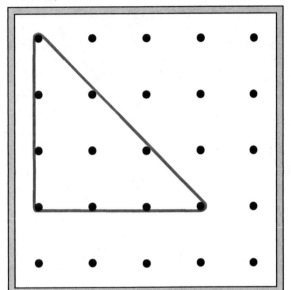

Example B

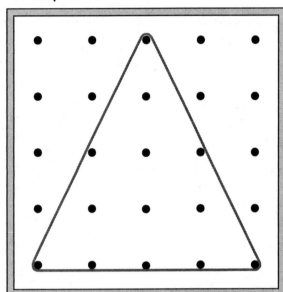

Example C

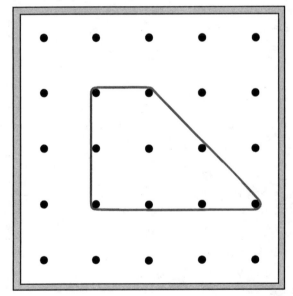

Hot Tip!

Remember that in setting expectations for working with tools that could potentially be misused (such as rubber bands), it is important to establish rules and overtly teach appropriate behavior for different settings, such as group work, independent work, and testing.

Phase of the 5E Instructional Model	Developmental Progression	Activity	Sense-Making	Discourse
Explore	**What concept(s) will the students explore?** *Positive, negative, zero, and undefined slope of lines; attributes of parallel and perpendicular lines; slopes of lines in polygons and 3-dimensional figures; and writing equations in slope intercept form.* **What vocabulary and symbols are needed for this phase?** *Slope* *Parallel ∥* *Perpendicular ⊥* *Slope formula* *Slope-intercept form* **What tools will I use in this phase of the lesson to allow the students to become directly involved in exploring the concepts?** *Grid paper, graphing calculators*	**What activity will I use to encourage students' exploration of the concept?** *Instead of going through the examples in the book, I will give them the coordinates in each example and prompt them to plot the points and graph the line on grid paper. They will determine the slope of the lines by counting and by using the slope formula. Then they will write the equation for the line.* *(See Examples 1-4 in the textbook lesson. Then refer to the following revised examples.)*	**What accommodations could be included in this phase?** *Before finding slope using the slope formula, prompt students to plot points on a coordinate grid, draw lines, and write the equation in slope-intercept form. Then connect with the slope formula. Using grid paper instead of only looking at the textbook examples incorporates multi-sensory learning.* **How could learning be made more accessible?** *Include needed vocabulary on the word wall.*	**Student – Student** *Students will work in groups. Although students will use their own grids, they will be encouraged to help each other as necessary.* **Student – Teacher** *Students will justify answers. Some justifications may be nonverbal.* **Teacher – Student** *Teacher will facilitate the activity as necessary.* **Facilitation questions** • *Can you identify the points and line on your graph?* • *Can you give the slope of the line?* • *How did you find the slope?* • *Is there another way you can find the slope?* • *What is the y-intercept?* • *What is the equation of the line in slope-intercept form?* • *Does the graph in the calculator match the graph on the grid paper?* • *Look at the table on the graphing calculator. Do the points on the graph on the grid paper correspond to those in the table?*

Hot Tip!

Remember it is important for students to explore. The Explore phase of a 5E lesson is not intended to be directly taught. The role of the teacher in this phase is that of a facilitator.

The next textbook lesson is to write equations of lines that form the sides of polygons graphed on a coordinate grid. I can bridge to the lesson by having students write the equations of the lines they have drawn.

Adapting a Textbook Lesson

Adapting Example 1

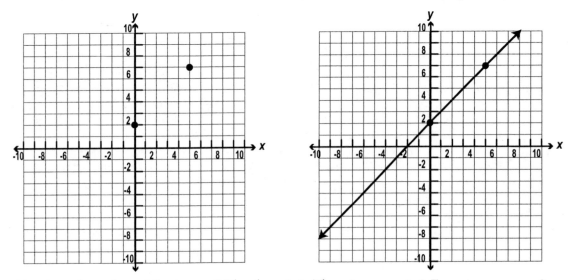

Use slope formula and "stairsteps." The slope is 1. The *y*-intercept is 2 Equation: $y = x + 2$.

Adapting Example 2

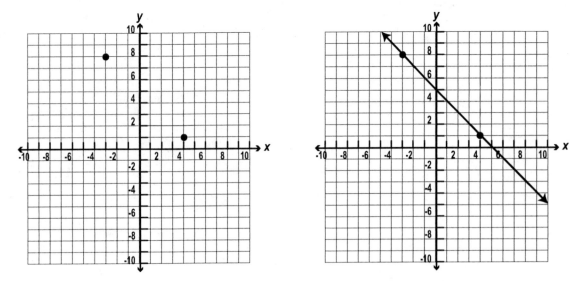

Use slope formula and "stairsteps." The slope is –1. The *y*-intercept is 5. Equation: $y = -x + 5$.

**Adapting a
Textbook Lesson**

Adapting Example 3

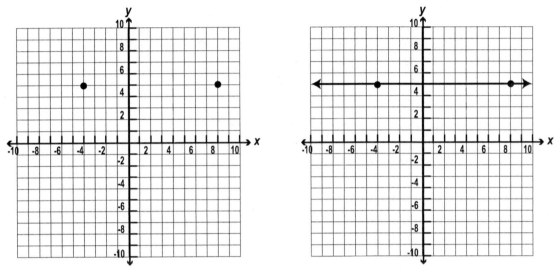

Use slope formula and "stairsteps." The slope is 0. The *y*-intercept is 5. Equation: *y* = 5.

Adapting Example 4

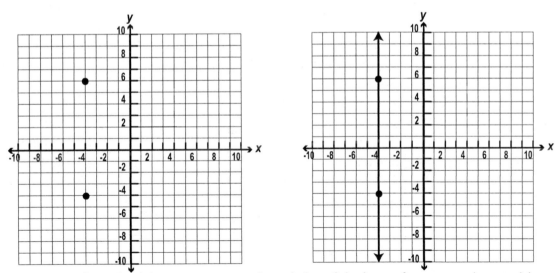

Use slope formula and connect to prior knowledge of the linear function and vertical-line test.
Slope is undefined. There is no *y*-intercept. Equation: *x* = −4

Phase of the 5E Instructional Model	Developmental Progression	Activity	Sense-Making	Discourse
Explain	**What connections are essential for the student to understand?** *Slope—* *positive* *negative* *slope of 0* *undefined slope* **What algorithms are connected to the concept?** *Slope formula*	**What misconceptions do I anticipate that may need to be corrected?** *Undefined slope compared to slope of 0.* **How will conceptual vocabulary be developed?** *Vocabulary organizer* *Concept definition map*	**What accommodations could be included in this phase?** *The vocabulary organizer and/or concept definition map will help students normalize concepts and vocabulary.* **How could learning be made more accessible?** *Remind students they may use the picture dictionaries and bilingual dictionaries in the classroom resource center.*	**Student – Student** *Students will explain work to each other.* **Student – Teacher** *Students will answer facilitation questions using both verbal and non-verbal communication.* **Teacher – Student** *Teacher will ask facilitating questions.* **Facilitation questions** • *What happens to the ordered pairs for vertices on the same line segment?* • *What conjectures can you make about slopes of lines?* • *What conjectures can you make about equations of lines?* • *How are the lines the same?* • *How are they different?*

Hot Tip!

Add to vocabulary organizers and definition concept maps, not only throughout a lesson but throughout a unit as a concept is developed.

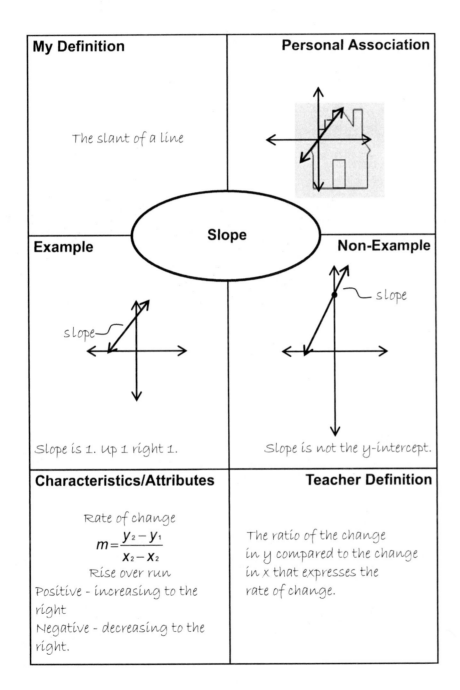

My Definition

The slant of a line

Personal Association

Slope

Example

slope

Slope is 1. Up 1 right 1.

Non-Example

slope

Slope is not the y-intercept.

Characteristics/Attributes

Rate of change

$$m = \frac{y_2 - y_1}{x_2 - x_2}$$

Rise over run

Positive - increasing to the right

Negative - decreasing to the right.

Teacher Definition

The ratio of the change in y compared to the change in x that expresses the rate of change.

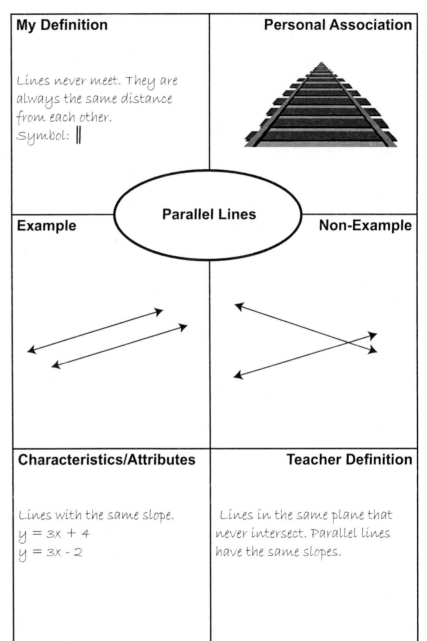

My Definition

Lines never meet. They are always the same distance from each other.

Symbol: ‖

Personal Association

Parallel Lines

Example

Non-Example

Characteristics/Attributes

Lines with the same slope.

y = 3x + 4

y = 3x - 2

Teacher Definition

Lines in the same plane that never intersect. Parallel lines have the same slopes.

Adapting a
Textbook Lesson

Adapting a Textbook Lesson

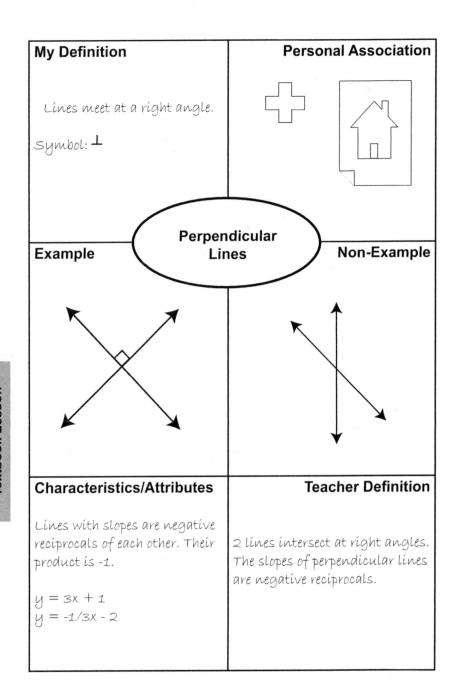

My Definition

Lines meet at a right angle.

Symbol: ⊥

Personal Association

Perpendicular Lines

Example

Non-Example

Characteristics/Attributes

Lines with slopes are negative reciprocals of each other. Their product is -1.

$y = 3x + 1$
$y = -1/3x - 2$

Teacher Definition

2 lines intersect at right angles. The slopes of perpendicular lines are negative reciprocals.

Knowledge doesn't just happen.

region 4
Educated Solutions

Phase of the 5E Instructional Model	Developmental Progression	Activity	Sense-Making	Discourse
Elaborate *Hot Tip!* *Since the concept is extended or expanded in the **Elaborate** phase of the lesson, it is appropriate to use different or additional tools.*	**How will the concept be applied or extended?** • *Exploring the slopes of parallel and perpendicular lines.* • *Writing equations of parallel and perpendicular lines in slope-intercept form.* **What tools or materials will be needed in this phase of the lesson?** *Patty paper* *Grid paper* *Graphing calculator* **Is there new vocabulary?** *Parallel lines* *Perpendicular lines* *Negative reciprocal* **How is the use of vocabulary encouraged?** *Students will add to vocabulary organizers and concept definition maps.* **What understanding must the student have to be successful with this phase of the lesson?** *Slope, slope formula, negative reciprocals, slope-intercept form of an equation* **How (if at all) must the algorithms be applied?** *The slope formula will be used to find slope of parallel and perpendicular lines.*	**What activity will I use to expand or elaborate on the concept?** • *Ask students to plot the points in Example 5 on grid paper. Then have them trace the axes and $\overrightarrow{AB}$ on patty paper. By keeping the y-axis aligned, they can translate the line to point Q. After students find the slope, ask them to find the y-intercept and write the equation of the lines.* • *Ask students to plot the points in Example 6 on grid paper. Then have them trace the axes and $\overrightarrow{AB}$ on patty paper. Rotate the $\overrightarrow{MN}$ patty paper so that the y-axis is over the x-axis, and slide the patty paper vertically so $\overrightarrow{MN}$ aligns with point R. After students find the slope, ask them to find the y-intercept and write the equation of the lines.* • *Use Example 7 as presented in the textbook lesson.*	**What accommodations could be included in this phase?** • *Use of patty paper and grid paper.* • *Use of the graphing calculator.* **How could learning be made more accessible?** *Heterogeneous grouping with attention to including peer support for Beginning and Intermediate ELL.*	**Student – Student** *Students will continue to work in their groups and will be encouraged to communicate with each other in solving the problems.* **Student – Teacher** *Students will be encouraged to respond to facilitation questions, which provide scaffolding support.* **Teacher – Student** *Teacher will ask facilitation questions to provide scaffolding support.* **Facilitation questions** • *What is the unknown or task to be completed?* • *What information or values to you have?* • *What information or values to you need?* • *Do you have a strategy to find the information or values you need?* • *Can you use more than one strategy with this problem?* • *What can you determine about the slopes of parallel lines?* • *What can you determine about the slopes of perpendicular lines?* • *How are the equations of parallel and perpendicular lines alike?* • *How are they different?*

Adapting a Textbook Lesson

Adapting a Textbook Lesson

Adapting Example 5

Step 1: Plot points A, B, and Q on a coordinate grid. Draw $\overrightarrow{AB}$.

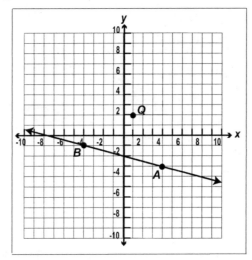
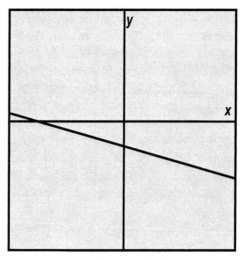

Patty paper representation
(if lifted from grid)

Step 2: Lay patty paper over the grid and trace the axes and line onto the patty paper.

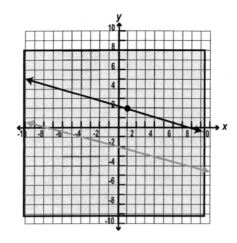

Step 3: Slide patty paper up keeping y-axis aligned until slanted line intersects (1, 2). Notice one of the points on the line is (-6, 4), the point found in Example 5 of the Textbook lesson.

Adapting Example 5

Step 1: Plot points M, N, and R on a coordinate grid. Draw $\overleftrightarrow{MN}$.

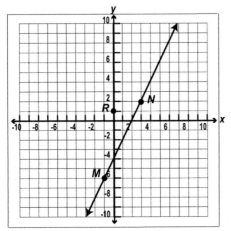

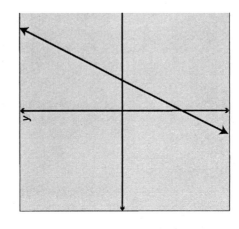

Step 2: Lay patty paper over the grid and trace the axes and line $\overleftrightarrow{MN}$ onto the patty paper.

Patty paper representation (if lifted from grid)

Step 3: Rotate the patty paper left 90°.

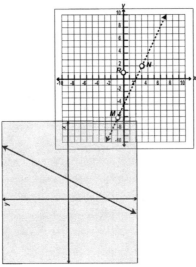

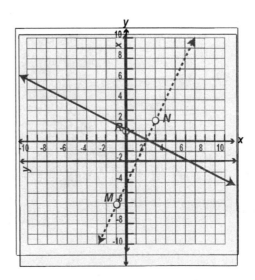

Step 5: Slide patty paper up keeping y-axis aligned until slanted line intersects (1, 2). Notice one of the points on the line is (-6, 4), the point found in Example 5.

Step 4: Position rotated patty paper.

137

Adapting a
Textbook Lesson

Adapting a
Textbook Lesson

Phase of the 5E Instructional Model	Developmental Progression	Activity	Sense-Making	Discourse
Evaluate	**What concept(s) are being addressed?** • *Finding slopes of lines, including parallel and perpendicular lines.* • *Investigate the properties of polygons, in this case to determine that the quadrilateral is a trapezoid with 2 right angles.* **What additional skills must the students have to successfully complete this phase?** *None* **What tools and materials will students need to complete the task?** *Coordinate grid paper, graphing calculator*	**What activity will I use in this phase to assess learning?** • *Performance assessment and 4 selected-response items (See following pages.)* • *Students will share answers using the* **Bonded Brains** *activity.*	**What accommodations could be included in this phase?** *Grid paper and graphing calculator will enhance student ability to solve the problems.* **How could learning be made more accessible?** *Allow access to picture and/or bilingual dictionaries.*	**Student – Student** *Students will work in their groups to solve the performance assessments. Groups will explain their findings using The Bonded Brains activity.* Since this lesson is typically taught early in the year in Geometry classes, and since the performance assessments are phased in (see Chapter 4), students will be allowed to work in their groups on the performance assessment. The selected-response items will be completed independently. **Student – Teacher** *As needed fro clarification* **Teacher – Student** *Teacher will monitor. Teacher will facilitate as groups share their work.*

Hot Tip!

If possible, enlist the support of the ESL teachers or bilingual aide for Beginning and Intermediate students.

Lucy ordered a pattern on the Internet to build a birdhouse. When the pattern arrived, the directions said:

1. On a coordinate system graph the points (–3, 3), (4, 2), (5, –1) and (–1, –3).
2. Connect the points in the order they are listed to form a quadrilateral.
3. Cut out the quadrilateral to use as the pattern for the right side of the birdhouse.

Lucy assumed the right side of the birdhouse would be in the shape of a rectangle. Is she correct? If she is incorrect, describe the quadrilateral that will be the right side of the birdhouse. Justify your description.

Possible student work

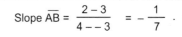

Identify points: **A** (-3, 3) **B** (4, 2) **C** (5, -1) **D** (-1, -3)

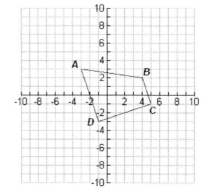

Slope $\overline{AB} = \dfrac{2-3}{4--3} = -\dfrac{1}{7}$.

Slope $\overline{BC} = \dfrac{-1-2}{5-4} = -\dfrac{3}{1}$.

Slope $\overline{CD} = \dfrac{-1--3}{5--1} = \dfrac{1}{3}$.

Slope $\overline{DA} = \dfrac{-3-3}{-1--3} = -\dfrac{3}{1}$.

Since $\overline{DA}$ and $\overline{BC}$ have the same slope, they are parallel. Since $\overline{CD}$ has slope that is a negative reciprocal of $\overline{DA}$ and $\overline{BC}$, $\overline{CD} \perp \overline{DA}$ and $\overline{CD} \perp \overline{BC}$.

The polygon that has only 2 sides parallel is a trapezoid. Since 1 side is perpendicular to 2 sides, there are 2 right angles.

a. (YES) NO   Student arrives at a correct solution?

	4	3	2	1
b. Conceptual Knowledge	x			
c. Procedural Knowledge	x			
d. Communication		x		

Sal graphed the isosceles trapezoid below.

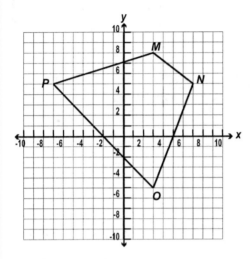

Which of the following is a true statement about $\overline{PN}$, the diagonal of trapezoid *MNOP*?

A   The slope of $\overline{PN}$ is undefined.

B   The slope of $\overline{PN}$ is negative.

C   The slope of $\overline{PN}$ is positive.

D   The slope of $\overline{PN}$ is zero.

Answer: D

A four-sided figure is shown on the coordinate grid below.

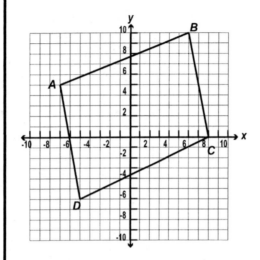

Which of the following best describes the figure?

A   *ABCD* is a quadrilateral.

B   *ABCD* is a rectangle.

C   *ABCD* is a parallelogram.

D   *ABCD* is a rhombus.

Answer: A

Which of the following sets of equations will form a right triangle?

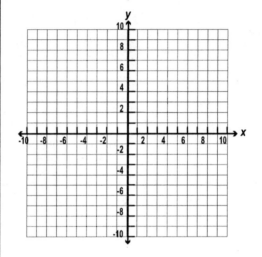

Which of the following best describes the figure?

A $y = \frac{1}{3}x + 2$, $y = -x + 7$, $y = \frac{1}{3}x + 5$

B $y = \frac{1}{4}x + 3$, $y = \frac{2}{3}x + 2$, $y = \frac{3}{2}x - 4$

C $y = -3x + 5$, $y = -3x - 5$, $x = 4$

D $y = \frac{1}{3}x + 2$, $y = -\frac{1}{3}x + 7$, $y = -3x + 5$,

Answer: D

B ig I deas

▲ It is possible to adapt traditional lessons with just a few changes of the strategies and practices that will enhance learning.

▲ You don't have to do it all immediately!

▲ When you are comfortable, move on to another phase.

Points to Ponder

At which stage am I today in implementing the 5E instructional model?

Considering my current stage, what could I do differently with the next lesson that would enhance student understanding, processing/participation, and communication?

What would I like to try next?

At which stage would I like to see myself next year?

Epilogue

Each person has an ideal, a hope, a dream which represents the soul. We must give to it the warmth of love, the light of understanding, and the essence of encouragement.

---Colby Dorr Dam

The mathematics team at the Region 4 Education Service Centers hopes the tools and strategies discussed in *Making Math Accessible for English Language Learners: Practical Tips and Suggestions* will help you in your efforts to make your students' hopes and dreams a reality.

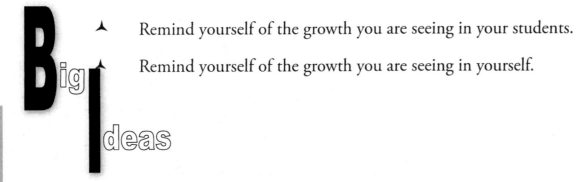

Big Ideas

▲ Remind yourself of the growth you are seeing in your students.

▲ Remind yourself of the growth you are seeing in yourself.

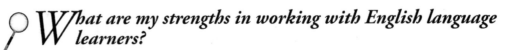

Points to Ponder

○ *What are my strengths in working with English language learners?*

○ *How can I play to my strengths?*

Appendix A

Appendix A: *Selected Glossary*

region 4
Educated Solutions

BICS--Basic interpersonal communications skills: the language ability required for social communication. It takes between one and three years to attain this basic level of oral proficiency.

Bilingual education--Students are allowed to develop language proficiency in two languages by receiving instruction in some combination of English and the student's primary language.

CALP--Cognitive academic language proficiency: Master of academic language necessary for students to succeed in context-reduced and cognitively-demanding content areas. It takes between five and 10 years for a second-language student to perform at grade level, without ELL support.

Cognates--Words in English closely related to the student's primary language.

Comprehensible Input--Adapting the level of language difficulty to the student's proficiency level to enable him to understand the content.

ELL--English language learner whose first language is not English.

ESL--English as a second language is an education approach in which English language learners are instructed in the use of English during specific class periods of the school day. There is typically little or no use of the primary language.

LEP--Limited English proficient: Term used by the federal government to identify students who are not proficient enough in English to succeed in English-only classrooms.

Primary language--First language learned in the home.

Pull-out instruction--Students leave the classroom for additional support to remediate, accelerate, or enhance instruction.

Realia--Real-life objects and artifacts used to enhance learning.

RTPE—The Reading Proficiency Test in English is the part of TELPAS that assesses the progress students are making in reading English.

Sheltered Instruction--Instructional approach in which students are main streamed and in which the teacher uses physical activities, visual aids, and the environment to teach vocabulary for concept development in math and other subjects.

TELPAS—Texas English Language Proficiency Assessment System for students who have limited English proficiency. It was developed by the Texas Education Agency to meet the federal testing requirements of the No Child Left Behind Act of 2001.

TOP—The Texas Observation Protocols use classroom observations to measure students' progress in listening, speaking, and writing in English. Each protocol is a part of TELPAS.

Appendix A: *Selected Glossary*

region 4
Educated Solutions

Appendix B

Appendix B: *Math English/Spanish Cognates*

region 4
Educated Solutions

English	Spanish	English	Spanish
activities	actividades	coordinate	coordenada
acute angle	ángulo agudo	cube	cubo
algebraic	algebraico	cylinder	cilindro
analyze	analizar	decimals	decimales
angles	ángulos	decisions	decisiones
application	aplicación	denominator	denominador
applies	aplicar	density	densidad
appropriate units	unidades apropiadas	dependent	dependiente
approximate	aproximado	describe	describir
architecture	arquitectura	diagram	diagrama
area	área	diameter	diámetro
art	arte	dimensions	dimensiones
bar graph	gráfica de barras	direct variation	variación directa
calendar	calendario	disciplines	disciplinas
capacity	capacidad	division	división
circle	círculo	domain	dominio
circumference	circunferencia	equal	igual
common	común	equation	ecuación
compare	comparar	equivalent	equivalente
complement	complemento	estimate	estimar, calcular
complementary	complementario	estimation	estimación
composite	compuesto	evaluate	evaluar
conclusions	conclusiones	exact	exacto
concrete	concreto	example	ejemplo
concrete models	modelos concretos	experiences	experiencias
cones	conos	experimental	experimental
congruent	congruente	exponents	exponentes
conjecture	conjetura	extend	extender
construct	construir	factorization	factorización
conversions	conversiones	factors	factores
convert	convertir	figures	figuras

Cognates

Appendix B: *Math English/Spanish Cognates*

Cognates

English	Spanish	English	Spanish
forms	formas	name	nombre
formulas	fórmulas	non-negative	no negativos
fractions	fracciones	numbers	números
function	función	numerator	numerador
generate	generar	objects	objetos
geometric	geométrico	obtuse	obtusos
geometric models	modelos geométricos	octagon	octágono
geometry	geometría	operations	operaciones
graph	gráfica	order	ordenar
hexagon	hexágono	ordered pairs	pares ordenados
hypotenuse	hipotenusa	organizing	organizar
identify	identificar	paper	papel
incorporate	incorporar	parabola	parábola
informal	informal	parallel	paralelo
interpreting	interpretar	parallelogram	paralelogramo
investigations	investigaciones	patterns	patrones
Iteration	repetición	pentagons	pentágonos
language	lenguaje	percentages	porcentajes
lateral surface area	area lateral de la superficie	perimeter	perímetro
line	línea	perpendicular	perpendicular
line graph	gráfica lineal	physical	físico
logical	lógico	pictograph	pictografía
mass	masa	plan	plan
mathematics	matemáticas	points	puntos
metric	métrico	polygons	polígonos
million	millón	polynomial	polinomio
minute	minuto	predictions	predicciones
mode	modo, moda (estadísticas)	price	precio
models	modelos	prime	primo
monomial	monomio	prisms	prismas
multiples	múltiplos	probabilities	probabilidades
multiplication	multiplicación	probability	probabilidad

English	Spanish	English	Spanish
problems	problemas	sphere	esfera
processes	procesos	statistics	estadística
properties	propiedades	strategy	estrategia
proportional	proporción	supplementary	suplementario
proportionality	proporcionalidad	symbols	símbolos
pyramids	pirámides	symmetry	simetría
Pythagorean Theorem	Teorema de Pitágoras	system of linear equations	sistema de ecuaciones lineales
quadratic	cuadrático	systematically	sistemáticamente
quadrilaterals	cuadriláteros	table	tabla
quantitative	cuantitativo	tables	tablas
quantitative reasoning	razonamiento cuantitativo	techniques	técnicas
radius	radio	technology	tecnología
range	rango (o alcance de una función)	temperature	temperatura
rotation	rotación	theoretical	teórico, hipotético
rational	racional	thermometer	termómetro
reasonable	razonable	transformation	transformación
reasoning	razonamiento	translation	translación
rectangular prism	prisma rectangular	transversal	transversal
relation	relación	trapezoid	trapecio
represent	representar	triangles	triángulos
representations	representaciones	triangular	triangular
results	resultados	units	unidades
rhombus	rombo	validate	validar
right angle	ángulo recto	variable	variable
round	redondear	vertex	vértice o cima
separate (adjective)	separado	vocabulary	vocabulario
separate (verb)	separar	volume	volumen
sequences	secuencias	y-intercept	intercepcion con el eje - y
simple event	evento simple		
situations	situaciones		
solution	solución		
spatial	espacial		

Cognates

Appendix B: *Math English/Spanish Cognates*

region*4*
Educated Solutions

Appendix C

Appendix C: *Responses to Tasks and Reflection*

Responses to Tasks and Reflections

Reflection 1.1

Sample response:

Some students transition to English very quickly because they are eager to learn, have supportive families, and encouraged by teachers who care and provide appropriate instruction.

Task 1.1

Case Study 1—Phong

Intermediate

Possible indicators:

- Relies on modified texts
- Becomes frustrated with contextual problems
- Has some understanding of the structure of the language, as indicated in the student's work

Case study 2—Randy

Advanced High

Possible indicators:

- Understands and uses academic language
- Demonstrates understanding of abstract mathematical concepts
- Functions on grade level
- Uses advanced sentence structure, including academic language, in justifying answers

Case study 3—Favian

Intermediate

Possible indicators:

- Uses social language
- Relies on prior knowledge
- Does not demonstrate that he understands academic language or abstract concepts

155

Appendix C: *Responses to Tasks and Reflection*

Case study 4—Belkiz

Beginning

Possible indicators:

- Relies on pictures, gestures, and translation
- Does not demonstrate that she understands the problem
- Uses only a couple of words, which may have been mimicked from the problem

Case study 5—Rocio

Advanced

Possible indicators:

- Can read unmodified texts, although she still needs some assistance
- Uses some descriptive language
- Communicates understanding of mathematical concepts on grade-level

Reflection 1.2

Sample response:

Beginning student

Challenge for student: Staying focused, having any idea about what is going on

Challenge for teacher: How can I help him understand the math when he doesn't understand anything I am saying?

Intermediate student

Challenge for student: Deciding what is important information in word problems

Challenge for teacher: Developing math vocabulary

Advanced student

Challenge for student: Understanding the dense, complex structure of word problems

Challenge for teacher: The student can solve problems with straight-forward text, but how do I help him decode more complex problems?

Advanced High student

Challenge for student: Succeeding in higher-level math courses to prepare for post-secondary education

Challenge for teacher: Helping the student "finesse" English and demonstrate mathematical proficiency at a high level of cognitive rigor

Reflection 2.1

Sample response:

1. Being greeted by my friendly teacher at the door
2. Being included in classroom activities
3. The teacher and/or students saying something in my first language

Reflection 2.2

Sample response:

I face the class when speaking, create an attractive classroom, and am patient, kind, and understanding.

I make a conscious effort to repeat important information and to pronounce students' names correctly.

I will start labeling objects and provide more wait time.

Task 2.1

Sample response:

Phong:

- SMILE.
- Speak slowly and distinctly. (Since she is still using modified texts, she will benefit from slower speech.)
- Allow tape recording of lessons.
- Use flexible grouping. (Since she is shy, she would probably participate more in a small group than with the whole class.)

Randy:

- Avoid slang and explain idioms. (He will benefit from explanations of idioms. For example, Jim paid $1000 for a computer and then some, meaning that he paid a little more than $1000 for the computer.)
- Use flexible grouping. (He could be a good group leader.)
- Have groups present work on chart paper. (Encourage expression of ideas using descriptive language and multiple representations of math concepts.)

Favian:

- Create a positive, non-threatening classroom environment. (Perhaps such an environment will encourage him to use English more frequently.)
- Use flexible grouping. (Since Favian understands English, working in a heterogeneous group will encourage him to use English.)
- Create word walls. (Word walls can help him build academic language and concepts.)

Appendix C: *Responses to Tasks and Reflection*

Belkiz:

- Label objects, speak slowly and distinctly, allow tape recordings, and ask for thumbs up/thumbs down responses to ease her transition to English.
- Find opportunities to bring the student's culture and language into class. (Since she has a strong tie to family and friends, providing connections to her community may increase her interest in class.)
- Use flexible grouping. (Since she is very social, working with others and developing classroom friends may appeal to her.)

Rocio:

- Use frequent, genuine praise. (This will help build her confidence to enhance her communication skills.)
- Create word walls. (Include academic vocabulary to help prepare her and other students for college.)
- Have students present work on chart paper. (This provides opportunities for both collaboration and feedback to increase communication of math concepts.)

region 4
Educated Solutions

Task 2.2

Sample response:

Affective Practices and Second Language Acquisition	Motivation	Age	Access to Language	Personality	Primary Language Proficiency	Cognitive Ability	Quality of Instruction
• SMILE	√						√
• Pronounce the student's name correctly.	√						√
• Be sure the student knows your name.	√						√
• Face the class when speaking.			√				√
• Speak slowly and distinctly.			√				√
• Avoid slang and explain idioms.			√				√
• Repeat important information in exactly the same words.			√				√
• Allow tape recordings of lessons.			√				√
• Label objects in the classroom (Examples: trash, overhead projector).			√				√
• Create attractive content-related bulletin boards.			√				√
• Provide plenty of wait time.			√				√
• Be patient, kind, understanding, and friendly.	√						√
• Utilize all 5 senses.			√				√
• Create a positive, non-threatening classroom environment.	√		√				√
• Find opportunities to bring the student's culture and language into class.	√		√				√
• Use frequent, genuine praise.	√		√				√
• Establish routines so students know what to expect.	√		√				√
• Post procedures and schedules.			√				√
• Use flexible grouping.	√		√				√
• Assign bilingual students as peer partners.	√		√				√
• Have groups present work on chart paper.	√		√				√
• Highlight contributions of mathematics from all cultures.	√		√				√
• Create word walls.			√				√
• Use dry erase boards (can be easily cut from bathroom tile board).	√		√				√
• Ask for thumbs up/thumbs down or other physical responses.	√		√				√

Appendix C: *Responses to Tasks and Reflection*

Reflection 2.3

Teachers have no control over the student's age, first language development, or cognitive ability. To some extent, she can influence student motivation with kindness and understanding and a nurturing classroom environment and, perhaps to a more limited extent, can even influence personality. She has greater influence over access to English while the student is in the classroom, but the factor over which teachers have the greatest control is effectiveness of instruction.

Task 3.1

Beginning:
- Incomprehensible with the exception of numerals
- Lack of graphics

Intermediate:
- Vocabulary (manufactures, decorative)
- Conceptual vocabulary (isosceles trapezoid)
- Pronouns
- Lack of action verbs (frequent use of has)
- Length of text

Advanced:
- Extraneous information
- Conditional tense in question (would be)

Advanced High
- Few, varying by student

Reflection 3.1

Responses will vary.

Task 3.2

My Definition	Personal Association
Lines in the same plane never meet. Symbol ‖	Insert graphic of railroad tracks and garden news.

Parallel Lines

Example	Non-Example

Characteristics	Teacher Definition
Lines with the same slope $y = 3x + 4$ $y = 3x + 2$	Lines in the same plane that do not intersect.

Task 3.3

Possible response:

Phong:

- Vocabulary organizer
- Think-alouds
- Word sorts
- Find Someone Who

Randy

- Vocabulary organizer
- Concept definition map
- Think-alouds
- Find Someone Who

Favian

- Cognates
- Vocabulary organizer
- Think-alouds
- Word sorts
- Find Someone Who

Belkiz

- Vocabulary organizer
- Word sorts
- Find Someone Who

Rocio

- Vocabulary organizer
- Concept definition map
- Think-alouds
- Find Someone Who

Reflection 3.2

Sample response:

I will use the vocabulary organizer continually to create an expanding word wall. I also have several Beginning Spanish-speaking students. I will use the cognates with them.

Task 4.1

Sample response:

Beginner:

- No. He cannot determine any mathematical concepts.

Intermediate:

- Probably not. He might think he should find perimeter because of the word length and add the numbers. A graphic would be helpful.

Advanced:

- Probably. He can determine that the bricks are made in the shape of isosceles trapezoids. Since the two legs of an isosceles trapezoid are the same length and he is given the perimeter, he can find the missing lengths. There is enough information for the student to solve although the extraneous information increases the rigor of the problem.

Advanced High:

- Yes. Even without a graphic, there is enough information for the student to solve the problem.

Reflection 4.1

Sample response:

Sometimes students "zone out." Some students avoid the situation by not coming to school or finding reasons to need to leave class. Others talk to their friends that speak the same language.
Some students get answers from other students while others just don't do the work.

Task 4.2

		Strategies	Manipulatives (specify which)	Technology	What Am I?	Example/ Non-Example	Concept Sorts	Window Panes	Quadrant Problem Solver	See-Plan-Do-Reflect	Bonded Brains
Phong	*Understanding*	Scaffolding Questions	Algebra tiles	Graphing calculator	√	√	√				
	Participating	Limit of length of assignments		√			√			√	√
	Communicating	Wait time		√			√			√	√
Randy	*Understanding*	Compare/Contrast		√	√	√		√			
	Participating	Think about his thinking		√				√	√		√
	Communicating	Justify answers		√				√	√		√
Favian	*Understanding*	Multiple Representatives	Algebra tiles	√	√	√	√				
	Participating	Use games		√			√			√	√
	Communicating	Use personal response boards		√						√	√
Belkiz	*Understanding*	Encourage note taking		√	√	√	√				
	Participating	Teach test-taking skills		√		√	√			√	√
	Communicating	Use complex sentences		√			√			√	√
Rocio	*Understanding*	Provide meaningful contexts	Algebra tiles	√	√	√		√			
	Participating	Work with group		√				√	√		
	Communicating	Assess non-verbally		√				√	√		√

Reflection 4.2

Over the course of the unit, I would have students work in groups frequently. We would collect data in a problem situation that can be described using a quadratic function in tabular form and then use the table to generate a graph and a function rule. We would use a graphing calculator to confirm the function rule over a scatter plot of the data, and then use the function rule to solve the original problem. After solving problems graphically, we would solve using algebraic methods, including using a concrete area model such as algebra tiles to factor and complete the square. We would use concept sorts with the steps for the first few examples. Only then would we use the quadratic formula. I would use think-alouds, utilize ample wait time, compare and contrast asking "why this" and "why not that" questions with example/non-example and scaffolding questions. I would also have students show their work on chart paper and/or personal response boards. I would have the students solve application problems using the See-Plan-Do-Reflect format.

Task 4.3

Phong

a. Yes No Student arrives at a correct solution?				
	4	3	2	1
b. Conceptual Knowledge			√	
c. Procedural Knowledge			√	
d. Communication			√	

Belkiz

a. Yes No Student arrives at a correct solution?				
	4	3	2	1
b. Conceptual Knowledge				√
c. Procedural Knowledge				√
d. Communication				√

Randy

a. Yes No Student arrives at a correct solution?				
	4	3	2	1
b. Conceptual Knowledge	√			
c. Procedural Knowledge	√			
d. Communication	√			

Rocio

a. Yes No Student arrives at a correct solution?				
	4	3	2	1
b. Conceptual Knowledge	√			
c. Procedural Knowledge	√			
d. Communication			√	

Favian

a. Yes No Student arrives at a correct solution?				
	4	3	2	1
b. Conceptual Knowledge			√	
c. Procedural Knowledge			√	
d. Communication				√

Appendix D

Appendix D: *Student Lesson*

Student Lesson

Toothpick Squares

Often toothpicks are used to create puzzles. Use toothpicks to build the puzzles below then try to find the solution.

Puzzle 1: Remove 3 toothpicks so there are 3 squares remaining. Sketch your solution.

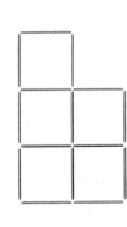

Solution

Puzzle 2: Remove 8 toothpicks so there are 4 squares remaining. Sketch your solution.

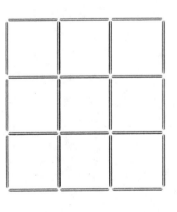

Solution

1. **Toothpicks can also be used to build models of terms in a sequence. What patterns do you notice in the sequence below?**

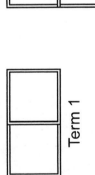

Term 1

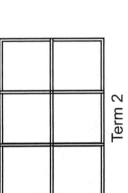

Term 2

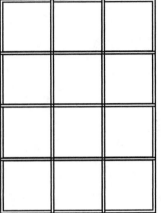

Term 3

region4
Educated Solutions

2. Use toothpicks to build the first three terms shown in the sequence in question number 1. Then build and sketch the models for terms 4 and 5.

Term 4

Term 5

3. Explain how you determined the models for terms 4 and 5.

4. How could you determine the number of squares in the model for any term number?

How Many Squares?

To determine the number of squares in the model for any term number you will use the data to determine a function rule to model your data. Then use your function rule to find the number of squares in any term.

1. **Use your models from the Toothpick Squares activity to complete the table below.**

Toothpick Squares

Term Number	Number of Squares
1	
2	
3	
4	
5	

2. **What patterns do you observe in your table?**

3. **Generate a scatter plot of your data. Identify your viewing window and sketch your graph.**

4. **What observations can you make about your graph?**

169 region4
Educated Solutions

5. Use the process column to develop an appropriate function rule to model your data.

Term Number	Process	Number of Squares

6. Test the rule over your scatter plot. Write your function rule and sketch your graph.

7. If this pattern continues, what will be the number of squares in the 15th term? Justify your answer.

8. If there are 650 squares in the model, what is the term number? Justify your answer.

How Many Toothpicks?

1. Use your models from the Toothpick Squares activity to determine the number of toothpicks necessary to build each model then complete the table below.

Toothpick Squares

Term Number	Number of Toothpicks
1	
2	
3	
4	
5	

2. What patterns do you observe in your table?

3. Generate a scatter plot of your data. Identify your window and sketch your graph.

4. What observations can you make about your graph?

region4
Educated Solutions

5. Develop an appropriate function rule to model your data.

Term Number	Process	Number of Toothpicks
1		
2		
3		
4		
5		
n		

6. Test the rule over your scatter plot. Write your function rule and sketch your graph.

7. If this pattern continues, what will be the number of toothpicks in the 15th term? Justify your answer.

8. If it takes 241 toothpicks to build the model, what is the term number? Justify your answer.

region 4
Educated Solutions

Square-to-Square

Orlando has the popular game, Square-to-Square, on his cell phone. Each time he successfully completes a game a new more difficult game board appears. The game boards for levels 1, 2, and 3 are show below.

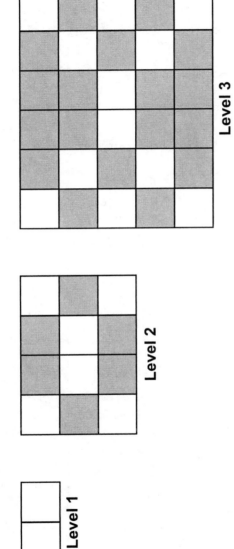

Level 1

Level 2

Level 3

If Orlando gets to level 10 how many shaded squares will his game board contain? Justify your answer.

region4
Educated Solutions

Part a) I arrived at a correct solution   YES   NO

Criteria	4	3	2	1
Part b) **Concept** **Understand the problem.**	I understood how all of the parts of the problem fit together, so I could make sense of the problem.	I understood all of the parts of the problem, and I made partial sense of the problem.	I understood some of the parts of the problem.	I showed little to no understanding of the important facts of the problem that would help me find the answer.
Part c) **Procedure** **Work the problem.**	I used an appropriate strategy. I connected how I needed to do the problem with what I understood about the problem and my selected strategy. I did all of my math steps correctly.	I used an appropriate strategy. I connected how I needed to do the problem with what I understood about the problem and my selected strategy. I did some of my math steps correctly. I did not arrive at a correct solution.	I used an appropriate strategy. I showed little connection between how I needed to do the problem and my selected strategy. I did some of my math steps correctly, but reached an incorrect or correct solution. (See Part a.)	I used an inappropriate strategy. My work had lots of mistakes.
Part d) **Communicate what you understand.** **Communicate how you worked the problem.**	I explained why I did what I did and supported my explanation with information from the problem. I used correct math vocabulary and notation.	I explained why I did what I did and supported my explanation with information from the problem. I used some correct math vocabulary and notation.	I gave little explanation of why I did what I did. I only explained what I did. I used some correct math vocabulary and notation.	I gave very little or no explanation of what I did. I used little or incorrect math vocabulary and/or notation.

Appendix E

Appendix E: *Cooperative Grouping*

region *4*
Educated Solutions

Cooperative Grouping for the ELL Classroom

Advanced Preparation:
* Cut and glue grouping shapes to index cards.
* Cut teacher cue cards.
* Laminate index cards and teacher cue cards (to make them last longer.)

How to Use:
The cooperative grouping cards need to be assigned based on the student's ability level using the following initial shape guide.

* Beginning English Language Learners –   △

* Intermediate English Language Learners –   □

* Advanced English Language Learners –   ○

* Advanced High English Language Learners –   ◁

Cards will need to be reassigned every two to three weeks based on the amount of cooperative grouping used during the time frame and the changing dynamics of the classroom. For example: the Beginning English Language Learners could be changed to the circle ○ .

Teacher cue cards will help facilitate smooth group transitions and aid the beginning learners in the classroom.

Helpful suggestion:
1. Using your seating chart and a second set of grouping shapes, put re-stickable glue on the back of the symbols and attach to assigned students' seat position.

2. Attach the grouping shape to the student's desk during the duration of the two to three week period.

Possible Groupings by ELL Classification:
Ability Groups:
Group by symbol (groups of 2, 3, and 4 can be used.)

Semi-Random groups:
* Groups of 2—Group by number.
  The pairs will group in such a way that the pairs of students will have one level between them.
  Example: a beginner student with an advanced student.

* Groups of 3—Group by letter.
  The groups will contain three different ability levels.

* Groups of 4—Group by sport.
  The groups will contain one student at each ability level.

Possible Mixed Groupings:
Distribute the set of grouping shapes randomly to the students during class and group as below.
* Groups of 2—Group by number.
* Groups of 3—Group by letter.
* Groups of 4—Group by sport.

region 4

Educated Solutions

A
1

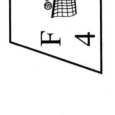

B
2

C
3

F
4

D
3

A
4

B
5

C
2

C
5

D
6

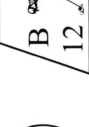

A
7

B
12

F
7

E
8

D
1

G
10

region4
Educated Solutions

 J 8

 E 6

 B 16

 I 14

 E 11

 G 9

 I 15

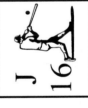 H 13

 F 10

 I 12

 H 14

 J 16

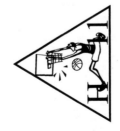 G 9

 H 11

 J 13

 A

region4

Educated Solutions

Shapes

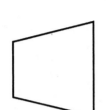
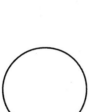

Sports

Alphabet

A B C D E F G H I J

Number

1 2 3 4 5 6 7 8 9 10 11 12 13 14 15 16

Shapes

Use for ability groups:

Beginning English Language Learners – △

Intermediate English Language Learners – ☐

Advanced English Language Learners – ○

Advanced High English Language Learners – ▱

> Switch around which symbol represents which level, because the students will figure out that the △ are the beginner students.

Sports

Use for groups of 4: one of each level.

- Beginner – Intermediate – Advanced – Advanced High

Alphabet

Use for groups of 3: Mixture will be of three different ability levels.

Number

Use for groups of 2: the pairs will group in such a way that the pair of students will have one level between them.

Examples:

- Beginner - Advanced combination
- Intermediate - High Advanced

region 4
Educated Solutions

Appendix F

Appendix F: *5E Lesson Plan*

region *4*
Educated Solutions

5E Lesson Plan				
TEKS:		Content Objective:	Language Objective:	Study/Metacognitive Objective:
Phases of the 5E Instructional Model	Developmental Progression	Activity	Sense-Making	Discourse
Engage	What tools or materials will I use in this phase to stimulate curiosity? What prior knowledge do I want to activate? Is there non-conceptual vocabulary that needs to be pre-taught?	What activity will I use to stimulate curiosity and activate prior knowledge?	What accommodations could be included in this phase? How could learning be made more accessible?	Student – Student Student – Teacher Teacher – Student Facilitating Questions

5E lesson Plan

187

Appendix F: *5E Lesson Plan*

Phases of the 5E Instructional Model	Developmental Progression	Activity	Sense-Making	Discourse
Explore	What concept(s) will the students explore? What vocabulary and symbols are needed for this phase? What tools will I use in this phase of the lesson to allow the students to become directly involved in exploring the concepts?	What activity will I use to encourage students' exploration of the concept?	What accommodations could be included in this phase? How could learning be made more accessible?	Student – Student Student – Teacher Teacher – Student Facilitation questions

Phases of the 5E Instructional Model	Developmental Progression	Activity	Sense-Making	Discourse
Explain	What connections are essential for the student to understand? What algorithms are connected to the concept?	What misconceptions do I anticipate that may need to be corrected? How will conceptual vocabulary be developed?	What accommodations could be included in this phase? How could learning be made more accessible?	Student – Student Student – Teacher Teacher – Student Facilitation questions

Appendix F: *5E Lesson Plan*

Phases of the 5E Instructional Model	Developmental Progression	Activity	Sense-Making	Discourse
Elaborate	How will the concept be applied or extended?	What activity will I use to expand or elaborate on the concept?	What accommodations could be included in this phase?	Student – Student
	What tools or materials will be needed in this phase of the lesson?		How could learning be made more accessible?	Student – Teacher
				Teacher – Student
	Is there new vocabulary?			Facilitation questions
	How is the use of vocabulary encouraged?			
	What understanding must the student have to be successful with this phase of the lesson?			
	How (if at all) must the algorithms be applied?			

Phases of the 5E Instructional Model	Developmental Progression	Activity	Sense-Making	Discourse
Evaluate	What concept(s) are being addressed? What additional skills must the students have to successfully complete this phase? What tools and materials will students need to complete the task?	What activity will I use in this phase to assess learning?	What accommodations could be included in this phase? How could learning be made more accessible?	Student – Student Student – Teacher Teacher – Student

5E lesson Plan

Appendix F: *5E Lesson Plan*

5E Lesson Plan

192 region 4 Educated Solutions

Appendix G

Appendix G: *References*

region *4*
Educated Solutions

Barton, M. & Heidema, C. (2002). *Teaching Reading in Mathematics,* (2nd edition). Aurora, CO: McREL.

Bye, M. (1975). "Reading in math and cognitive development." Unpublished manuscript. (ERIC Document Reproduction Service No. ED 124 (26).

Crandall, J. (1985). The language of mathematics: the English barrier. In *Issues in L2: Theory as Practice, Practice as Theory*. Delaware Symposium on Language Studies.

Cummins, J. (1981) Primary language instruction and the education of language minority students. *Schooling and Language Minority Students: A Theoretical Framework*. Los Angeles Evaluation, Dissemination and Assessment Center, School of Education, California State University, Los Angeles.

Dale, T. (1992). Integrating mathematics and language learning. *The Multicultural Classroom*. White Plains, NY: Longman Publishing.

Davey, B. (1983). *Think aloud: Modeling the cognitive processes of reading comprehension*. Journal of Reading.

Echevarria, J., Vogt, J, and Short, D. (2004). *Making Content Comprehensible for English Learners*. Boston: Pearson Education.

Genesee, F. and Gándara, P. (1999) Bilingual Education Programs: A Cross-National Perspective. *Journal of Social Issues*. Vol. 55 Issue 4.

Halliday, M. (1978). *Language as Social Semiotic: The Social Interpretation of Language and Meaning*. Baltimore: University Park Press.

Haynes, J. (2003) Challenges for ELLs in content area learning. *Helping Mainstream Teachers in Content Area Classes*. Retrieved from http://www.everythingesl.net.

Jarrett, D. (1999) *The Inclusive Classroom: Teaching Mathematics and Science to English Language Learners: It's Just Good Teaching*. Northwest Regional Educational Laboratory.

Kessler, C. (1985). Processing mathematics in a second language: Problems for LEP children. *Issues in L2: Theory as Practice, Practice as Theory*. Delaware Symposium on Language Studies.

Krashen, S. (1982). *Principles and practice in second language acquisition*. NY: Prentice-Hall.

McLaughlin, M. (1993). *A classroom guide to performance-based assessment*. Princeton, MJ: Houghton-Mifflin.

McLaughlin, M. and Vogt, J. (1996) *Portfolios in teacher education*. Newark, DE: International Reading Association.

National Council of Teachers of Mathematics (2000). *Principles and Standards for School Mathematics*. Reston, VA: NCTM.

National Council of Teachers of Mathematics (2005). A Position Paper: Closing the Achievement Gap. Reston, VA:NCTM

References

Appendix G: *References*

National Research Council. (2002). *Helping children learn mathematics.* Washington, DC: National Academy Press.

National Symposium on Learning Disabilities in English Language Learners (2003). Symposium summary. Retrieved from http://www.ed.gov/about/offices/list/osers/products/ld-ell/index.html.

Polya, G (1957. *How to Solve it*: Princeton, NJ: Princeton University Press.

Region 4 Education Service Center (2004). Coordinate Transformation Lesson. *TAKS Mathematics Preparation, Grade 11 Exit.* Houston, TX: Region 4 ESC.

Region 4 Education Service Center (2005). Quadratic Functions. *Accelerated Curriculum, Grade 11 Exit.* Houston, TX: Region 4 ESC.

Romo, H. (1993). Mexican Immigrants in High Schools: Meeting Their Needs. ERIC. Document Reproduction Service No. ED357905.

Schumann, J.H. (1978). *The Pidginisation Process: A Model for Second Language Acquisition.* Rowley MA: Newbury House.

Secada, W.G., & De La Cruz, Y. (1996). *Teaching mathematics for understanding to bilingual students.* Charleston, WV: ERIC Clearinghouse on Rural Education and Small Schools.

Stiggins R. (1970). *Student-centered classroom assessment.* Upper Saddle River, New Jersey: Prentice-Hall, Inc.

Texas Education Agency Austin. Division of Student Assessment (2002). Texas student assessment program technical digest for the academic year 2002-03. Retrieved from http://www.tea.state.tx.us/student.assessment/resources/techdig/contents.pdf.

Texas Education Agency Austin. Division of Curriculum (2004a). Bilingual and English as a Second Language (ESL) Program Models. Retrieved from http://www.tea.state.tx.us/curriculum/biling/ProgramModels-revised110304.ppt#422,39,Program Personnel.

Texas Education Agency Austin. (2004b). Texas English Language Proficiency Assessment System (TELPAS) 2004 Sample Reports and Interpretive Guide. Retrieved from http://www.tea.state.tx.us/student.assessment/telpas/telpas_guide.pdf.

Texas Education Agency Austin. (February 2005a) Chapter 89. Adaptations for Special Populations. Subchapter BB. Commissioner's Rules Concerning State Plan for Educating Limited English Proficient Students.

Texas Education Agency Austin. Division of Student Assessment(2005b). Texas English Language Profiency Assessment System. Retrieved from http://www.tea.state.tx.us/studentassessment/Reporting/results/summary/sum05/telpas/telpas_statewide05.pdf.

Trowbridge, L. and Bybee, R. (1996). *Teaching Secondary School Science: Strategies for Developing Literacy.* Englewood, Cliffs NJ: Merril.

Wiggins, G. (1998). *Educative assessments: Designing assessments to inform and improve student performance.* San Francisco, California: Jossey-Bass.